the FABULOUS FURRY
FREAK
BROTHERS
IN THE IDIOTS ABROAD

KNOCKABOUT

Foreword

IT IS ANOTHER BUSY AFTERNOON IN THE THIRTY-SEVENTH FLOOR EDITORIAL DEPARTMENT OF THE RENOWNED **RIP OFF PRESS, INC.,** HIGHRISE OFFICES.

HERE'S ANOTHER PIECE OF *FREAK BROTHERS* MAIL!

THIS ONE APPEARS TO BE WRITTEN IN **MUD** ON **WAXED PAPER!**

LET'S SHOW THEM TO MR. **SHELTON** AND MR. **MAVRIDES!**

THANK YOU, MS. LOWER-TODD!

I CAN BARELY MAKE IT OUT... (GRUNT!) MORE SARCASM... "ARE THOSE SELF-STYLED **FABULOUS** (ALTHOUGH **UNDENIABLY FURRY**) **FREAK BROTHERS** STILL ALIVE? I CAN'T FIND THEIR **BOOKS** FOR SALE **ANYWHERE** ANY MORE! COME TO THINK OF IT, I NEVER COULD FIND THEIR BOOKS WHEN THEY **WERE** ALIVE, EITHER! SIGNED, **FORMER FAN.**"

HERE'S ONE MORE PIECE, SIR! IT'S IN **LIPSTICK** ON **BLUE-LINE NOTEBOOK PAPER!**

"WHO GIVES A **HAMSTER FART** FOR THOSE **AGING HIPPIES,** THOSE **RELICS OF THE SIXTIES,** THOSE OLD **TROGLODYTES** THE **FREAK BROTHERS?** WHY DON'T YOU WRITE SOMETHING **FUNNY,** LIKE TEN THOUSAND THINGS TO DO WITH A **DEAD GARFIELD?**"

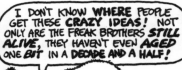

I DON'T KNOW **WHERE** PEOPLE GET THESE **CRAZY IDEAS!** NOT ONLY ARE THE FREAK BROTHERS **STILL ALIVE,** THEY HAVEN'T EVEN **AGED** ONE **BIT** IN A DECADE AND A HALF!

IT SOUNDS **BIZARRE,** BUT IT'S **TRUE!** WHILE THE **REST** OF US ARE DOWN HERE **ROTTING** AND **SHRIVELING MERRILY AWAY,** THAT TRIO OF **IRRESPONSIBLE RASCALS** IS OFF ON SOME **MYTHICAL ASTRAL PLANE** DOING WHATEVER THEY WANT TO DO, AND NEVER GETTING SICK OR SHOWING ANY SIGNS OF MORTALITY AT ALL!

IT'S **REALLY** BEGINNING TO **BUG** ME!

I WISH SOMEONE WOULD TEACH THOSE GUYS SOME OF THE **CRUEL FACTS OF LIFE** FROM THE **REAL LIVE WORLD!**

IN FACT, —HEH HEH— THAT GIVES ME AN **IDEA!** WE CAN JUST HAVE THE **COMPUTOON® 8000** INFECT THE FREAK BROTHERS WITH A **SUDDEN, IRRATIONAL DESIRE TO TRAVEL!**

ISN'T THIS A MARVELOUS MACHINE? IT WRITES ALL OF OUR STORIES FOR US!

WHY DON'T YOU **PUNCH** THAT IN, MAVRIDES?

...S·U·D·D·E·N... ...I·R·R·A·T·I·O...

HA HA HA! IT'S GONNA SCATTER THAT BUNCH OF HAREBRAINS **ALL OVER** THE **SURFACE** OF THIS **PLANET!** IT'LL PROBABLY EVEN SEND **FAT FREDDY** SOMEPLACE WHERE HE WON'T BE ABLE TO FIND A **MACDONALD'S!** GUFFAW!

THAT SPACED-OUT GANG OF DRUGGIES WON'T LAST **THIRTY MINUTES** OUTSIDE THE U.S.A.! THEY'LL STARVE TO DEATH, OR BE MURDERED FOR SURE! NO MORE FREAK BROTHERS, HA HA!

NOW I'LL BE FREE TO MOVE TO GREENLAND!

THAT'S RIGHT! IT'S MY LIFE'S AMBITION TO MOVE TO **GREENLAND** AND GROW **CITRUS FRUIT!** YOU KNOW, I ALREADY **OWN** SOME **PROPERTY** UP THERE! BOUGHT IT THROUGH THE **COMPUTOON® 8000,** AS A MATTER OF FACT!

THAT LAND OUGHT TO BE WORTH A **LOT OF MONEY** NOW, WITH THE **REAL ESTATE BOOM** AND ALL, DON'T YOU THINK? I'VE NEVER **SEEN** THE PLACE ACTUALLY, BUT THE **COMPUTER** TELLS ME IT'S AS **GREEN** AS **ANY PLACE IN GREENLAND!** SOUNDS NICE, HUH?

SORRY, GENTLEMEN, BUT THE COMPUTER FOULED UP AND PUT **NEXT YEAR'S** DATE ON YOUR PAYCHECKS! I HOPE YOU DON'T **MIND!** YOU CAN **WAIT,** CAN'T YOU?

CERTAINLY! I'M ALREADY MAKING **MORE MONEY** THAN I KNOW WHAT TO DO WITH! HOW ABOUT YOU, MAVRIDES?

I DON'T MIND! IT'S A **PRIVILEGE** JUST TO **BE** HERE! THE **COMPUTOON® 8000** DOES MOST OF THE ACTUAL WORK, **ANYWAY!**

LOOK! IT'S **FINISHED** WITH THE **WHOLE STORY ALREADY!** LET'S GET GOING ON THE **ROUGH SKETCHES** AND WE'LL BE **ALL THROUGH** IN A **HALF-HOUR!**

...AND SO THE FREAK BROTHERS ARE OFF ON THE **GRAND TOUR!** AND WHITHER THEY GO, ONLY THE **COMPUTOON® 8000** SHALL KNOW.

THE FABULOUS FURRY FREAK BROTHERS in "**THE IDIOTS ABROAD**" by GILBERT SHELTON and PAUL MAVRIDES with color separations by GUY COLWELL; Copyright © 1987 by Rip Off Press, Inc., and Gilbert Shelton. All rights reserved under international copyright law. No part of this book may be reproduced without permission of copyright holder. Printed in Denmark. Published by Knockabout, 10 Acklam Road, London W10 5QZ. Not for sale in the U.S.A. or Canada.

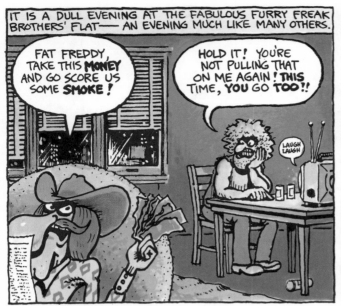

IT IS A DULL EVENING AT THE FABULOUS FURRY FREAK BROTHERS' FLAT — AN EVENING MUCH LIKE MANY OTHERS.

FAT FREDDY, TAKE THIS **MONEY** AND GO SCORE US SOME **SMOKE**!

HOLD IT! YOU'RE NOT PULLING THAT ON ME AGAIN! **THIS** TIME, **YOU** GO **TOO**!!

LAUGH LAUGH

WELL, IF YOU'RE **BOTH** GOING, I'D LIKE TO GO, **TOO**!

I'M REALLY TIRED OF ALL THIS SLEAZY SNEAKING AROUND IN THE SLUMS! LET'S GO TO **COLOMBIA** AND BUY THE STUFF AT THE **SOURCE**!

FOR THE PRICE OF A **KILO** OF **WEED**, WE COULD GET **THREE** ROUND TRIP TICKETS TO **BOGOTA**!

...AND ONCE WE GET THERE, THE STUFF IS PRACTICALLY **FREE**, I UNDERSTAND!

WHAT'RE WE WAITING FOR? LET'S PACK OUR BAGS!

SPROING

I GOT MY STUFF!

ME TOO! WHERE'S PHINEAS? HE'S TAKING HOURS!

OKAY! I'M READY!

HEY! WE'RE ONLY GOING TO BE **GONE** FOR A **COUPLE** OF **WEEKS**!

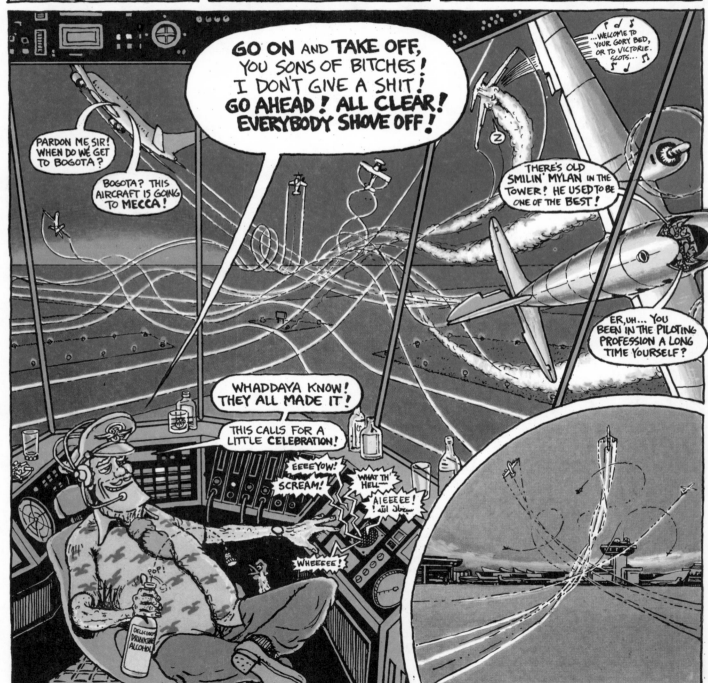

THAT NIGHT, SOMEWHERE OVER CENTRAL AMERICA:

THERE ARE REGIONS OUT HERE THAT ARE SO REMOTE THEY'VE NEVER EVEN BEEN MAPPED! NO ONE KNOWS WHAT COUNTRY THEY'RE IN! NO ROADS TO THE OUTSIDE WORLD! ONLY A FEW INDIANS LIVE AROUND THESE PLACES! SO WE BUILT SETTLEMENTS!

WE FLY IN EVERYTHING WE NEED! WE'VE EVEN BUILT A LANDING STRIP AT ONE OF THE SITES!

OKAY, GET READY TO START DROPPING THE STUFF!

I DON'T SEE ANYBODY DOWN THERE!

WELL, THEY'RE DOWN THERE! DROP!

THERE'S THE AIRSTRIP!

I DON'T SEE ANY AIRSTRIP!

IT'S ONLY A COUPLE OF HUNDRED FEET LONG...

GOOD LORD! (GASP!)

BUT IT GOES UP AT THE END...

ARRRGH! (CHOKE!)

AS THE C-46 ROLLS TO A STOP, A NUMBER OF FIGURES EMERGE FROM THE NEARBY DENSE JUNGLE FOLIAGE.

ATTACHING A ROPE TO THE TAIL WHEEL, THEY SWING THE AIRCRAFT AROUND AND PULL IT UP THE INCLINE.

CAMOUFLAGE VINES ARE THEN THROWN OVER THE PLANE, MAKING IT ALMOST TOTALLY INVISIBLE FROM THE AIR.

WOW! IT'S A LITTLE PARADISE! A REGULAR GARDEN OF EDEN!

WHATEVER THAT BOOGER WAS, IT'S NOT ON THE RADAR ANY LONGER!

EITHER THEY MUSTA CRASHED OR ELSE IT WAS SOME KINDA PHANTOM BLIP!

IT'S TIME TO GET BACK! WE'RE GETTING LOW ON FUEL!

AIR FORCE F-15's! BUT THEY CAN'T SEE US DOWN IN THIS LITTLE BASIN! SO FAR WE'RE UNCONTAMINATED BY ANY CONTACT WITH THE FORCES OF AUTHORITY!

MAYBE IT WOULD BE A GOOD IDEA TO GET A FEW HOURS REST AND THEN GO ON TO BOGOTA TOMORROW NIGHT!

NO ONE KNOWS WE'RE HERE EXCEPT THE LOCAL INDIANS, AND WE HAVE A SPECIAL RELATIONSHIP WITH THEM!

WHAT ARE ALL YOU PEOPLE DOING HERE?

SOME OF US ARE INTO ARCHITECTURE, SOME ARE INTO TECHNOLOGIES LIKE SOLAR AND GEOTHERMAL HEAT COLLECTION, AND SOME ARE INTO GARDENING!

SOME OF US JUST LIKE TO SIT AROUND IN OUR HOT TUBS!

THAT SOUNDS LIKE FUN!

YOU CAN STAY HERE AT THE GUEST HOUSE! I HAVE MY OWN PLACE OVER ON THE OTHER SIDE OF THE RAVINE!

GOOD NIGHT! SEE YOU IN THE MORNING!

GUEST HOUSE

IT'S WARM AND DAMP DOWN HERE! MAYBE I CAN FIND SOME MUSHROOMS!

WOW! IT'S A HUGE STONE COVERED WITH ALL SORTS OF LITTLE PICTURES! IT LOOKS LIKE IT MIGHT BE SOME SORT OF HISTORICAL CALENDAR!

IT... IT'S JUST LIKE A COMIC STRIP! I CAN ACTUALLY READ IT! HERE'S A MASTODON HUNT BACK DURING THE ICE AGE! I WONDER HOW FAR ON IT GOES? HERE'S THE SPANISH INVASION OF AMERICA... AND UP HERE... AN AUTOMOBILE?! SKYSCRAPERS?? AND FLYING MACHINES ??!?

GOOD LORD! IT'S A PICTURE OF ME! HOW COULD WHOEVER CARVED THIS HAVE KNOWN ABOUT ME? AND PHINEAS AND FREDDY!

HA HA HA! IT'S THE STORY OF WHEN FAT FREDDY ATE ALL SIXTEEN OF THE HASH COOKIES THAT PHINEAS BAKED FOR THE BIG PARTY! AND HERE'S WHEN WE SOLD THE KILO OF DOG SHIT TO NORBERT THE NARK FOR $2,000!

(GASP!) HERE I AM IN THE PLANE COMING HERE YESTERDAY!!! AND HERE I AM IN THIS CHAMBER, LOOKING AT THIS VERY STONE!!

...AND NOW.. UH-OH! SOMEONE'S COMING!

THAT GUY DIDN'T COME UP THIS WAY, DID HE? WE CAN'T HAVE HIM FINDING OUT ABOUT "THE END!"

BY THE TIME FRANKLIN REACHES THE FIRST REMOTE VILLAGE, HIS CLOTHING IS VIRTUALLY INDISTINGUISHABLE FROM THE NATIVE GARB.

YOU GOT ANY COLD BEER, AMIGO?

NO BEER HERE! COSTS TOO MUCH!

MEANWHILE, A MILITARY CONVOY IS APPROACHING THE VILLAGE FROM THE DOWNHILL DIRECTION.

MOVE QUICKLY! WE MUST HAVE A FLAT PLACE FOR THE HELICOPTER TO LAND! THERE! CUT DOWN THOSE PLANTS IN THAT LITTLE PATCH THERE!

OKAY! BRING 'ER IN!

IT'S A GIFT FROM COLONEL GAVILAN, SIR! IT'S A NEW ARMORED CADILLAC LIMOUSINE!

FUMP FUMP FUMP FUMP FUMP FUMP FUMP

VILLAGERS! THIS IS COLONEL GALLITO! ASSEMBLE AT ONCE IN THE TOWN GARDEN SO THAT YOU MAY MARVEL AT THE NEW SHINY AUTO THAT WAS A GIFT FROM THE FAMOUS COLONEL GAVILAN TO MY OWN ILLUSTRIOUS SELF!

NO ONE HEARD ME!! FIRE A BURST INTO THE AIR, CADET-COLONEL PICHON!

FUMP FUMP FUMP FUMP

FIREWORKS! OH BOY! MAYBE I'VE ARRIVED JUST IN TIME FOR SOME SORT OF FIESTA!

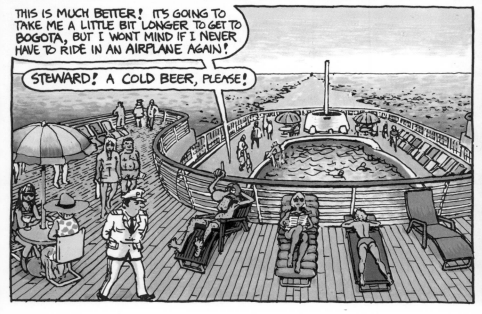

HEY, BOSS! IT'S THE "COLUMBO II" OUT OF HOUSTON HEADED FOR BARANQUILLA, COLOMBIA! SHE LOOKS LOADED! LET'S TAKE HER!

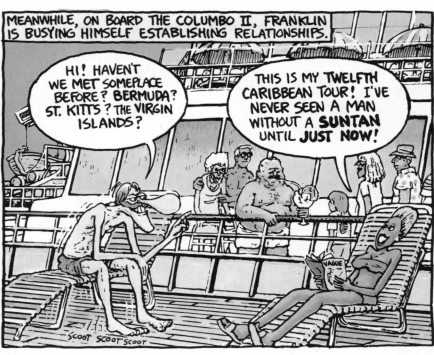

MEANWHILE, ON BOARD THE COLUMBO II, FRANKLIN IS BUSYING HIMSELF ESTABLISHING RELATIONSHIPS.

HI! HAVEN'T WE MET SOMEPLACE BEFORE? BERMUDA? ST. KITTS? THE VIRGIN ISLANDS?

THIS IS MY TWELFTH CARIBBEAN TOUR! I'VE NEVER SEEN A MAN WITHOUT A SUNTAN UNTIL JUST NOW!

SCOOT SCOOT SCOOT

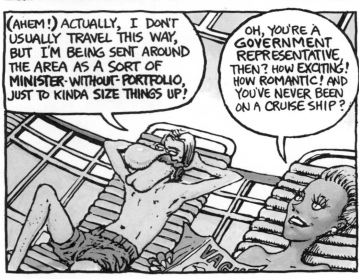

(AHEM!) ACTUALLY, I DON'T USUALLY TRAVEL THIS WAY, BUT I'M BEING SENT AROUND THE AREA AS A SORT OF MINISTER-WITHOUT-PORTFOLIO, JUST TO KINDA SIZE THINGS UP!

OH, YOU'RE A GOVERNMENT REPRESENTATIVE THEN? HOW EXCITING! HOW ROMANTIC! AND YOU'VE NEVER BEEN ON A CRUISE SHIP?

PERSONALLY, I'D RATHER BE DRIVING A CAR, BUT... WE HAVE TO BE MINDFUL OF OUR IMAGE NOWADAYS! WE CAN'T HAVE THE LATINOS THINKING OUR SYSTEM IS ECONOMICALLY UNSOUND OR ANYTHING LIKE THAT!

I'VE NEVER EVEN MET A "LATINO" BEFORE! DO YOU SPEAK SPANISH?

WELL, I COULD LEARN SPANISH IF I WANTED TO, BUT ALL THE PEOPLE WE DEAL WITH DOWN HERE INSIST ON SPEAKING ENGLISH ANYHOW! IT'S THE INTERNATIONAL LANGUAGE OF BIG BUSINESS! I WOULDN'T WANT TO EMBARRASS THEM BY SPEAKING SPANISH!

IT'S SO REASSURING TO FINALLY HAVE PEOPLE DOWN HERE WHO KNOW HOW TO ACT!

MATERIAL WEALTH MEANS AN AWFUL LOT IN TODAY'S TURBULENT WORLD! THAT'S OUR NATION'S STRENGTH, AND IT'S OUR DUTY TO FLAUNT IT!

LISTEN, HOW WOULD YOU LIKE TO SEE MY STATEROOM? THEY HAD TO THROW OFF A COUPLE OF DEMOCRATS TO GET IT FOR ME!

OHHH, I'D LOVE TO! YOU GOVERNMENT PEOPLE ARE SOOOOOO SMOOOOOTH!

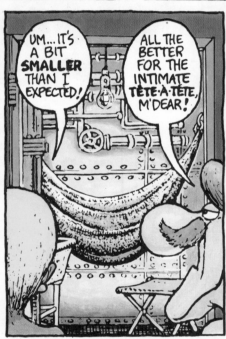

AT A LARGE MILITARY COMMAND POST A FEW KILOMETERS AWAY...

IT'S "ANDRÉ THE HYENA" AND HIS SQUADRON OF INTERNATIONAL TERRORISTS, ALL RIGHT! THEY WERE TRYING TO ENTER ON A CHARTER FLIGHT, DISGUISED AS FOOTBALL HOOLIGANS!

WE INTERCEPTED THEM JUST AS THEY WERE LANDING AT GLASGOW! THEY CLAIM TO HAVE A ½-KILOTON, HAND-CARRIED NUCLEAR DEVICE! WE DIDN'T REALIZE JUST HOW TECHNICALLY ADVANCED THEY HAD BECOME IN THE LAST COUPLE OF YEARS!

THEY ALMOST SNUCK IN OUR BACK DOOR! CAN THE LOCAL UNIT KEEP THEM PINNED DOWN UNTIL WE GET SOME COMMANDOS THERE?

IF WE CAN BREAK OUT OF THEIR CIRCLE, WE CAN LOSE OURSELVES IN THE DARK! IT'LL HELP TO PUT ON SOME OF THIS BLUE CAMOUFLAGE MAKE-UP!

WHAT ARE WE GOING TO DO WITH THIS BLOKE? HE SEEMS TO HAVE ADOPTED US! HE MUST BE MENTALLY RETARDED OR SOMETHING!

WHY ARE WE HIDING? I CAN'T UNDERSTAND YOU GUYS WHEN YOU TALK! SHOULD I PAINT MYSELF BLUE, TOO? I NEVER HEARD OF THAT! I'M BEGINNING TO THINK YOU GUYS MIGHT NOT EVEN BE FOOTBALL FANS LIKE YOU TOLD ME!

MAYBE WE CAN USE HIM AS A HOSTAGE IF WORSE COMES TO WORST! HE MIGHT BUY US A FEW PRECIOUS SECONDS!

THAT COULD BE THE DIFFERENCE BETWEEN SUCCESS AND FAILURE! HERE, HELP ME MOVE THE BOMB OVER THERE!

HEY! YOU GUYS ARE ACTUALLY SOCCER FANS, AREN'T YOU? ALL THIS TIME I WAS THINKING YOU GUYS WERE TALKING ABOUT FOOTBALL!

YOU FOREIGN PEOPLE DON'T KNOW DOODLEYSQUAT ABOUT REAL FOOTBALL!

SOCCER PLAYERS AREN'T EVEN ALLOWED TO HIT EACH OTHER! WHAT KIND OF SISSY GAME IS THAT?

DOGCATCHER ONE TO COMMAND CENTRAL! WE ARE APPROACHING GLASGOW RUNWAY TWO FROM SOUTH!

PREPARE TO JUMP!

WHAT KIND OF GUY WOULD PLAY A SERIOUS SPORT IN SHORT PANTS?

SET WHATCHAMACALLIT AT DELTA THIRTY-THREE...

...W-H-A-T-C-H-M-A...

...AND ALL YOU EVER DO IS KICK THE THING AROUND! THAT'S THE MOST BORING THING I EVER HEARD OF!

OKAY, NOW WHAT?

CLICK!

OH NO! WE'RE **TOO LATE!** THEY'VE GOTTEN AWAY!

WE WERE AMBUSHED BY A HORDE OF **PICTISH WARRIORS,** COLONEL, ALL **BLUE** AND **TATTOOED** AND 'ORRIBLE THEY WERE, RETURNED FROM THE **MURKY PAST,** SIR, TO WREAK **PAGAN VENGEANCE** UPON US ALL!

IN THE DARKNESS AND CONFUSION, AND FUELED BY THE EXCITEMENT OF FOREIGN TRAVEL (AS WELL AS SEVERAL DOZEN STRAIGHT WHISKIES), FAT FREDDY QUICKLY OUTSTRIPS HIS COMPANIONS THE TERRORISTS, DESPITE BEING BURDENED BY THE HALF-KILOTON ATOMIC BOMB DISGUISED AS A KICKBALL.

JEEZ! I NEVER KNEW SOCCER BALLS WERE SO **HEAVY!** HOW DO THE GUYS KEEP FROM **BREAKING THEIR TOES?**

IT IS ONLY WHEN HE FINALLY STOPS AT A MACDONALD'S TO EAT, THAT HE BEGINS TO UNDERSTAND WHAT HAS OCCURRED.

THE NOTORIOUS TERRORIST **ANDRE THE HYENA** AND HIS GANG BROKE OUT OF A POLICE TRAP AT **GLASGOW AIRPORT** EARLIER THIS EVENING WHERE THEY WERE ATTEMPTING TO PASS THROUGH CUSTOMS DRESSED AS FOOTBALL FANS! AN EXTENSIVE DRAGNET HAS BEEN PUT OUT FOR THE FUGITIVE MEN, WHO WERE RUMORED TO HAVE BEEN CARRYING SOME SORT OF SMALL BUT POWERFUL **BOMB,** AND WHO WERE LAST SEEN CLAD IN THE COLORS OF F.C. **PARTICK THISTLE, RED** AND **YELLOW...**

!

$\frac{2}{4}$

NONE OF THESE **BIKES** ARE **LOCKED UP!** WHAT'S THE *MATTER* WITH THESE PEOPLE HERE, **ANYHOW?**

ALL THROUGH THE NIGHT FAT FREDDY PEDALS, ON COUNTRY ROADS ACROSS MOOR AND FEN, ELUDING THE VAST MANHUNT HE HAS SET OFF ONLY BY DINT OF HIS CUSTOMARY EXTRAORDINARILY **GOOD LUCK**...

HERE COMES **ANOTHER** ONE DRIVING ON THE WRONG SIDE OF THE ROAD! GOD, WHAT AN **INSANE COUNTRY!** HOW THE HELL AM I GOING TO GET TO **BOGOTA, COLOMBIA**, FROM THIS PLACE?

...UNTIL FINALLY, IN THE PRE-DAWN GLOOM, HE PERCEIVES THE DIM FORM OF AN ANCIENT STONE CASTLE RISING DARKLY FROM THE MIST.

I'VE GOT TO HIDE!

THERE, CROUCHED IN A HIDDEN AND PARTIALLY SHELTERED CORNER OF THE RUIN, THE CONFUSED, EXHAUSTED, AND DESPAIRING FREAK BROTHER BUILDS A TINY FIRE TO TRY TO FIGHT OFF THE COLD.

NEARBY, IN A DARKENED NOOK, A PAIR OF EYES SPARKLES. THEY BELONG TO A SMALL SPIDER.

THE SPIDER HAPPENS TO BE A DESCENDANT, MANY GENERATIONS REMOVED, OF THE VERY SPIDER WHICH PROVIDED THE INSPIRATION FOR SCOTLAND'S HERO AND FOUNDER, **ROBERT BRUCE.**

THE BRUCE, YOU MAY RECALL, FOUND HIMSELF ONE TIME IN MUCH THE SAME SITUATION AS FAT FREDDY NOW FINDS HIMSELF: IN DESPERATE FLIGHT AND HIDING FROM HIS ENEMIES.

AS HE PONDERED CAPITULATION AND SURRENDER, HIS GAZE FELL UPON A SPIDER WHO WAS TRYING TO BUILD A WEB ACROSS A LARGE OPENING.

AGAIN AND AGAIN, THE SPIDER TRIED UNSUCCESSFULLY TO LEAP WITH HIS FILAMENT ACROSS THE GAP. ROBERT BRUCE WATCHED, FASCINATED, FOR A LONG, LONG PERIOD OF TIME.

FINALLY, AFTER MANY A TRY, THE SMALL SPIDER SUCCEEDED IN REACHING THE OPPOSITE LEDGE AND WAS ABLE TO GO ON AND COMPLETE HIS WORK. STIRRED DEEPLY BY THE EXAMPLE SET BY THE SIMPLE ARACHNID, BRUCE REGAINED HIS SPIRITS AND WENT ON TO DEFEAT THE ENGLISH AT BANNOCKBURN IN 1314.

FAT FREDDY, ON THE OTHER HAND, HAS A **PATHOLOGICAL ABHORRENCE** OF **ALL TYPES** OF SPIDERS.

KEEEEEEEEYARRRGH!!

...AND THE BOMB IN THE FOOTBALL SKIN, FORGOTTEN, BEGINS TO ROLL SLOWLY DOWN THE GRASSY SLOPE...

...AND DISAPPEARS NOISELESSLY INTO THE DARK, DEEP WATERS OF THE FAMOUS **LOCH NESS.**

FREDDY'S THOUGHTS, HOWEVER, HAVE ALREADY TURNED TO THE SUBJECT OF... STARVATION

THAT BARTENDER DIDN'T WANT TO ACCEPT MY AMERICAN DOLLARS! I CERTAINLY HOPE THAT'S NOT GOING TO BE AN OBSTACLE TO MY BUYING SOMETHING TO EAT!

IS THAT SOMETHING TO EAT? I CAN'T TELL!

BANGERS & MASH 50p
Plaice £1.50
GAMMON 2.00
CRISPS 35p   SCONES 2

LOST, CONFUSED, AND AFRAID TO BE SEEN IN PUBLIC, FREDDY TRAVELS THE BACK ROADS AT NIGHT SUBSISTING ON VEGETABLES GLEANED FROM PRIVATE GARDEN TRACTS.

ALL THEY GROW IS BRUSSELS SPROUTS!

(WHIMPER!) (GAGG!)

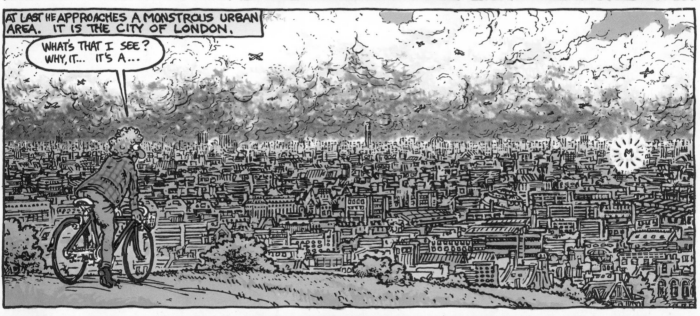

AT LAST HE APPROACHES A MONSTROUS URBAN AREA. IT IS THE CITY OF LONDON.

WHAT'S THAT I SEE? WHY, IT... IT'S A...

IT'S AN AMERICAN RESTAURANT!

HAMBURGER

(PANT!) (PUFF!) I'LL HAVE FOUR BURGERS, THREE LARGE FRIES, TWO APPLE PIES AND A LARGE COKE AND A LEMONADE!

HEY, WOW! YOU HAVE BEER HERE?! GIVE ME A BEER, TOO!

WHAT TOWN IS THIS?

THAT'LL BE FIVE QUID, FIFTY P, SIR!

YOU TAKE AMERICAN MONEY, DON'T YOU?

CERTAINLY, SIR! NINETY DOLLARS!

AT THE SAME TIME, IN A CONCRETE-WALLED COMMAND BUNKER DEEP BENEATH A HILLSIDE...

ANDRÉ THE HYENA HAS SLIPPED OUT OF OUR GRASP! AND HE'S CARRYING A NUCLEAR BOMB! THIS COULD BE ULTIMATE DISASTER FOR THE ENTIRE FREE WORLD!!

I WANT TO KNOW WHO IS RESPONSIBLE!

IT WAS HIS FAULT!

NO, IT WAS HIS FAULT!

NO! HIS FAULT!

HIS FAULT!

THEIR FAULT!

AND THEIR FAULT TOO!

IT WAS THAT GUY'S FAULT OVER THERE!

NO! THAT BUNCH OF GUYS BY THE DOOR!

IT WAS HIM!

NO, IT WAS HIM!

IT WAS EVERYONE OVER THERE!

THEIRS!

THOSE!

HIS!

HERS!

ALL THOSE DOWN THERE!

HIS FAULT AND HIS FAULT!

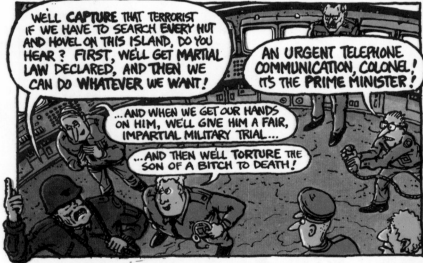

WE'LL CAPTURE THAT TERRORIST IF WE HAVE TO SEARCH EVERY HUT AND HOVEL ON THIS ISLAND, DO YOU HEAR? FIRST, WE'LL GET MARTIAL LAW DECLARED, AND THEN WE CAN DO WHATEVER WE WANT!

...AND WHEN WE GET OUR HANDS ON HIM, WE'LL GIVE HIM A FAIR, IMPARTIAL MILITARY TRIAL...

...AND THEN WE'LL TORTURE THE SON OF A BITCH TO DEATH!

AN URGENT TELEPHONE COMMUNICATION, COLONEL! IT'S THE PRIME MINISTER!

THEY'RE ORDERING US TO LAY OFF ANDRÉ! THEY'RE GOING TO ANNOUNCE THAT HE'S BEEN CAPTURED AND EXECUTED! THEY'RE SAYING IF WORD OF A NUCLEAR BOMB BECAME PUBLIC, THE PEOPLE IN THE CITIES WOULD BE LIKELY TO COMPLETELY PANIC!

THOSE IMBECILIC CIVILIANS! ANDRÉ DOESN'T WANT TO BOMB CITIES! HE'S AFTER ONE OF OUR "PEACE CENTERS"!

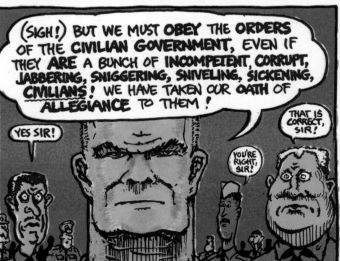

(SIGH!) BUT WE MUST OBEY THE ORDERS OF THE CIVILIAN GOVERNMENT, EVEN IF THEY ARE A BUNCH OF INCOMPETENT, CORRUPT, JABBERING, SNIGGERING, SNIVELING, SICKENING, CIVILIANS! WE HAVE TAKEN OUR OATH OF ALLEGIANCE TO THEM!

YES SIR!

THAT IS CORRECT, SIR!

YOU'RE RIGHT, SIR!

JUST AN INSTANT BEFORE HE WOULD HAVE EXPIRED OF SEASICKNESS, FAT FREDDY IS WASHED UP ON A WIDE, UNBROKEN STRETCH OF SANDY BEACH.

HUFF HUFF PUFF POFF

WINDMILLS! THAT MEANS HOLLAND! AND AMSTERDAM! AND LEGAL HASHISH!

AFTER FRESHENING UP A BIT IN A CANAL, FAT FREDDY MANAGES TO HITCH A RIDE IN A TANKER TRUCK TO AMSTERDAM.

WOW! YOU HAVE SHELL OIL HERE, TOO?

IT'S A DUTCH COMPANY! WE ALL SPEAK ENGLISH, THOUGH!

THERE, HE SOON LOCATES THE "DISTRICT."

WHERE'S THE HASHISH PARLOR?

IT'S MY LIFETIME DREAM COME TRUE! LEGAL DOPE! I'LL STAY HERE FOREVER!

THE FLYING DUTCHMAN

THE FLYING DUTCHMAN

UH-OH! I HAVE BARELY ENOUGH MONEY FOR FOOD! BUT I CAN'T HAVE COME ALL THIS WAY FOR NOTHING!

GIVE ME FIFTY CENTS WORTH OF HASHISH AND A DOLLAR OF COCAINE!

WE ARE TOLERANT PEOPLE HERE, MISTER! WE CAN TOLERATE JUST ABOUT ANYTHING BUT A TOURIST WITH NO DOUGH! COME, HAVE A RIDE TO THE BORDER!

GOSH! I'VE NEVER RIDDEN IN ONE OF THESE PORSCHES BEFORE!

POLITIE

IN BELGIUM, THEY ARE LESS TOLERANT.

WE'RE GIVING YOU A FREE TRIP TO THE FRENCH LINE!

GEE! I'VE NEVER RIDDEN IN A CATTLE CAR BEFORE!

THE NEXT MORNING FAT FREDDY AWAKENS IN AN EXTENSIVE RAILWAY SWITCHYARD.

I'VE SEEN THAT BUILDING BEFORE!

IT WAS IN A PAINTING AT THE K-MART!

THERE'S A GREAT BIG EIFFEL TOWER! THIS MUST BE PARIS, THE CITY OF GOURMETS!

"RESTAURANT"?

"MENU"?

SAY, THIS FRENCH ISN'T SO HARD TO READ, AFTERALL!

PAIN?

POISONS?

CRUDITES?*

GOLLY, THESE FRENCH PEOPLE SURE EAT SOME WEIRD SHIT!

*pain = bread
poisson = fish
crudites = vegetables

FORTUNATELY, THEY HAVE AMERICAN FOOD HERE TOO!

GIMME FIVE BIG MAX, FOUR LARGE FRIES, THREE APPLE PIES, TWO COKES, A LEMONADE, AND...

ANDRÉ!

WE'VE BEEN ATTENDING YOUR ARRIVEMENT, MON AMI! ZE FUTBOL, S'IL VOUS PLAÎT!

SCREECH

MAYBE I CAN LOSE THEM IN THIS THEATRE, JUST LIKE LEE HARVEY OSWALD!

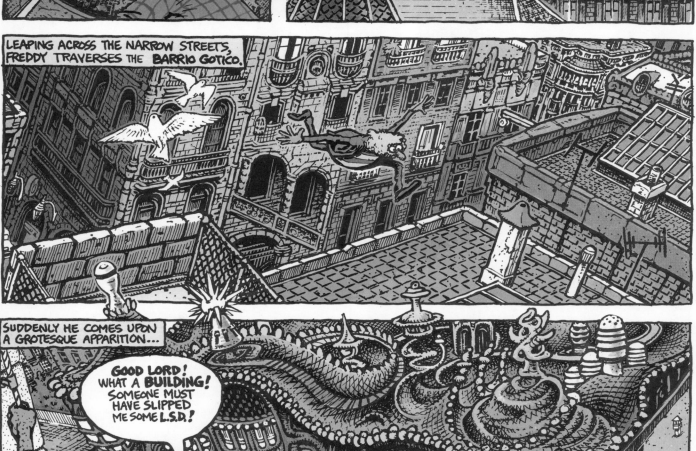

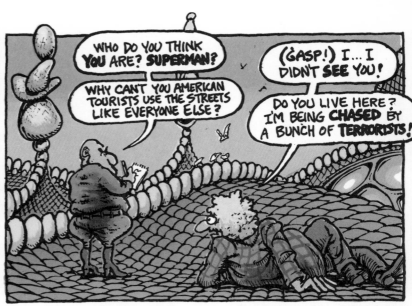

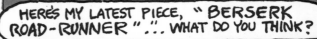

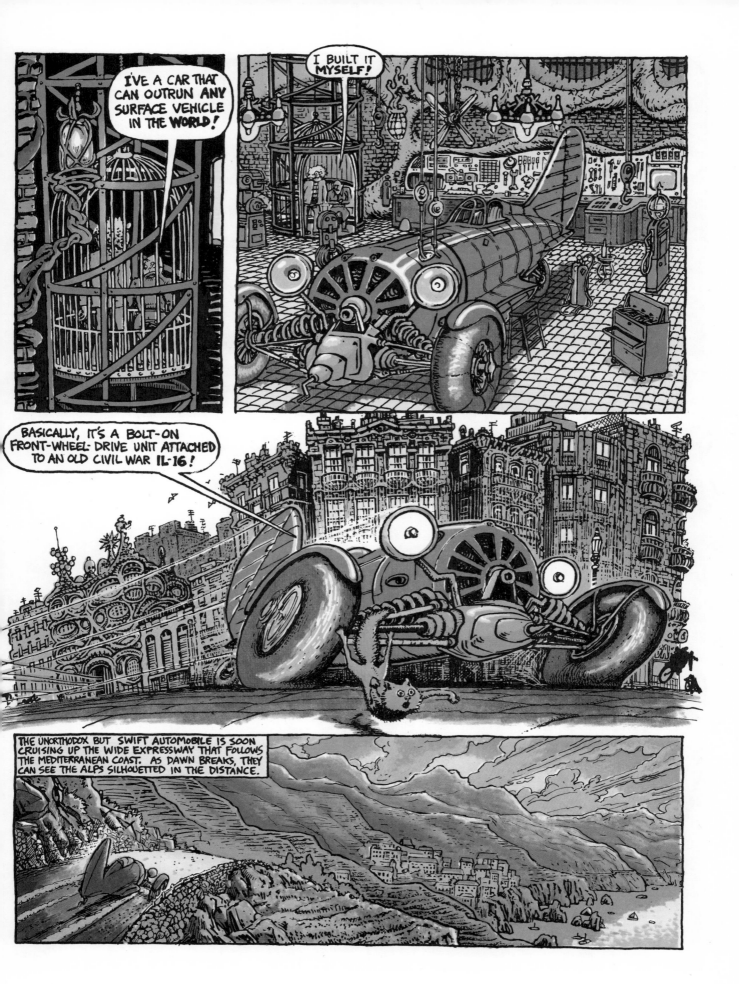

IS THAT PLACE YOURS, TOO? WHAT **ARE** YOU ANYWAY, SOME KIND OF HEREDITARY ARISTOCRAT?

NOPE! I'VE MADE EVERYTHING I OWN THROUGH **HARD WORK!**

OVER A LEISURELY BREAKFAST, PABLO PEGASO TELLS FAT FREDDY SOME DETAILS OF HIS CAREER.

I EARN MONEY FROM MY **INVENTIONS!** SOME OF THEM, LIKE THE **AIRPLANE HIGHWAY CONVERTER,** NEVER REALLY CAUGHT ON, BUT OTHERS LIKE THE **YOGURT-SLICING MACHINE** WERE QUITE SUCCESSFUL!

WOW! YOU INVENTED SLICED YOGURT?

IN THE CIVIL WAR I WAS A MESSENGER IN THE SERVICE OF THE **ANARCHIST MILITIA!** WE WERE ALLIED WITH THE **COMMUNISTS** AT THE TIME...

THERE WAS THIS RUSSIAN, COLONEL **KAKOV...** HE'S IN THE **INNER CIRCLE** BACK IN MOSCOW NOW...

COMMUNISTS? WOW! I'VE ALWAYS WONDERED ABOUT COMMUNISM! I ALWAYS WANTED TO VISIT **MOSCOW!** BUT I'M ON MY WAY TO **BOGOTA, COLOMBIA!** I WAS SUPPOSED TO MEET MY FRIENDS THERE, BUT I RAN OUT OF **MONEY!**

WHAT? YOU'RE RUNNING AROUND, ALL OVER EUROPE, WITH SOME MYSTERIOUS GANG OF GUYS SHOOTING AT YOU, AND YOU DON'T EVEN HAVE ANY **MONEY?** THAT MAKES NO SENSE AT ALL!

IT MUST BE MY **MAGNETIC PERSONALITY!**

YOUR FRIENDS MUST BE **WORRIED** ABOUT YOU! LET ME **HELP** YOU TOWARD YOUR **DESTINATION!**

THERE ARE COMMUNISTS IN COLOMBIA, TOO, IF THAT'S WHAT YOU WANT!

WOW! THANKS! THAT'S REALLY **GENEROUS** OF YOU!

AH! HERE'S THE **TAILOR** WITH YOUR **NEW CLOTHES!** I HAD HIM MAKE **TWELVE** COPIES OF WHAT YOU WERE **WEARING!**

EVENTUALLY, HOWEVER, HE FINDS HIMSELF TRAPPED IN THE LAST CAR OF THE TRAIN. BY THIS TIME THEY ARE SOMEWHERE IN RURAL EASTERN POLAND.

СТОП КРАН

EMERGENCY STOP

THIS IS CLEARLY AN EMERGENCY!

SQUEEEEEEEEEEE

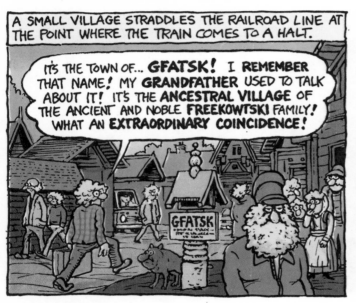

A SMALL VILLAGE STRADDLES THE RAILROAD LINE AT THE POINT WHERE THE TRAIN COMES TO A HALT.

IT'S THE TOWN OF... GFATSK! I REMEMBER THAT NAME! MY GRANDFATHER USED TO TALK ABOUT IT! IT'S THE ANCESTRAL VILLAGE OF THE ANCIENT AND NOBLE FREEKOWTSKI FAMILY! WHAT AN EXTRAORDINARY COINCIDENCE!

GFATSK

MAYBE I CAN SEARCH OUT A COUSIN OR SOMETHING!

GREETINGS, MY GOOD MAN! MY NAME IS FREEKOWTSKI!

FREEKOWTSKI?

FREEKOWTSKI!

WHAT FAT FREDDY'S GRANDFATHER NEVER TOLD HIM WAS JUST EXACTLY WHY HIS ANCESTORS LEFT THEIR ANCIENT ANCESTRAL HOME...

OW! OW! I'LL TAKE MY CHANCES ON THE TRAIN!

THE UNSCHEDULED STOP ALLOWS OUR HERO TO SLIP INTO THE FIRST CAR, ELUDING THE CUSTOMS INSPECTORS.

46

SOME HOURS LATER, HE ARRIVES AT MOSCOW'S CENTRAL STATION.

ALL MIGHT HAVE PASSED WITHOUT INCIDENT IF HE HAD NOT WALKED BY THE STATE MUSEUM OF VODKA WHILE LOOKING FOR A HOTEL.

МУЗЕЙ ВОДКИ

GEE, THANKS FOR ALL THE FREE SAMPLES, FELLAS! (HIC!)

I STILL DON'T BELIEVE VODKA IS MADE OUT OF POTATOES!

(HIC!)

OOPS!

HIC!

CRASH!

HIC!

THUMP!

HIC!

CLATTER!

HIC!

WHAM!

A SMALL BLUEJEAN RIOT ENSUES.

AIEEEE!! AMERICANSKI DESIGNER BLUE JEANS!

HORRORSHOW!
HORRORSHOW!
HORRORSHOW!
HORRORSHOW!

I'LL GIVE YOU EIGHT HUNDRED RUBLES FOR ONE PAIR!

A THOUSAND RUBLES!

TEN THOUSAND!

GASP! THEY TOOK EVERY SINGLE PAIR OF MY PANTS! I'M FORTUNATE TO HAVE ESCAPED WITH MY LIFE!

WHAT'S ALL THE EXCITEMENT? WHY... IT'S A PARADE! IT'S THE INFAMOUS MAY DAY PARADE!

48

Part 2

KNOCKABOUT
Collections

The first volume of the complete
Freak Brothers in paperback edition.

The second volume of the complete
Freak Brothers in paperback edition.

GILBERT SHELTON calls him 'The second
ugliest thing on Earth'. This is the first
collection of the 'Hog of Steel'.

While the Freak Brothers are globe
trotting communist cockroaches fight
around the beleaguered Fat Freddy's Cat.

THE CAST of CHARACTERS

AND A ONE-SENTENCE SYNOPSIS OF THE STORY SO FAR

Phineas — Fat Freddy — Freewheelin' Franklin

THE FABULOUS FURRY FREAK BROTHERS

THE **FABULOUS FURRY FREAK BROTHERS** HAD REALLY TRIED TO GO TO BOGOTA SOME TIME AGO AND HAD ACTUALLY GOTTEN AS FAR AS THE AIRPORT, TRAILED UNOBSERVED BY THE NOTORIOUS **NORBERT THE NARK**, WHEN THEY BECAME SEPARATED, **FREEWHEELIN' FRANKLIN** GOING FIRST TO CENTRAL AMERICA IN A RESTORED WWII C-46 PILOTED BY A MYSTERIOUS WOMAN WHO IS A MEMBER OF A **GROUP OF SURVIVALISTS**, THEN ALMOST BEING SHOT BY THE LEADER OF A RIGHT-WING DEATH SQUAD, **COLONEL GALLITO**, AND HIS SON **CADET-COLONEL PICHON**, THEN BEING CAPTURED BY A BOATFUL OF **MODERN-DAY PIRATES OF THE CARIBBEAN** AND FINALLY BEING SOLD AS A SLAVE IN AFRICA, WHILE **FAT FREDDY** WAS CONDUCTING A HIGH-SPEED CHASE SCENE THROUGHOUT EUROPE, PURSUED BY **ANDRÉ THE HYENA** AND HIS **GANG OF INTERNATIONAL TERRORISTS**, FREDDY HAVING UNWITTINGLY RUN OFF WITH ANDRÉ'S NUCLEAR BOMB AND LOST IT IN LOCH NESS, AND AFTER HAVING BEEN RESCUED BY THE ANARCHIST ARTIST-INVENTOR **PABLO PEGASO**, MAKING AN UNPLANNED SIDE TRIP TO MOSCOW, WHERE HE IS ARRESTED FOR SOME TRIVIAL OFFENSE.

You talkin' to me? You talkin' to me?

NOTORIOUS NORBERT THE NARK

ANDRÉ THE HYENA
AND HIS GANG OF INTERNATIONAL TERRORISTS

COLONEL CORNBELT AND THE AUTHORITY of the NEW ERA

ARTIST AND INVENTOR
PABLO PEGASO
ANARCHIST AND GOURMET

SMILIN' MYLAN
THE HAS-BEEN AIR ACE

THE SURVIVALISTS of the CENTRAL AMERICAN MOUNTAINS & THEIR INDIAN FRIENDS

THE LOCH NESS MONSTER

MEANWHILE, AT THE HEADQUARTERS OF **COLONEL CORNBELT**, A HEATED DRESSING-DOWN IS TAKING PLACE.

YOU! WE'VE TRACED THE **GENERAL BREAKDOWN** IN OUR OPERATION TO YOU! I'M DEMOTING YOU TO THE RANK OF **PRIVATE!**

YOU CAN'T! I'M ALREADY A PRIVATE!

COLONEL, SIR, ONE OF OUR OPERATIVES REPORTS ANDRÉ IS IN BARCELONA!

WELL, AT LEAST HE CAN'T CAUSE US ANY TROUBLE FROM THERE!

C.O.

DAMN THE GOVERNMENT! DAMN THE PRESS! AND DAMN ALL THOSE PEOPLE WHO BELIEVE WHATEVER THEY READ! IF I WERE IN COMMAND OF THIS CHICKENSHIT CONTINENT THERE WOULD BE SOME CHANGES MADE, I GUARANTEE YOU!

WIN AT... ULTRA·MEGA·MEDIA NEWS SOURCE TIMES

ANDRE THE HYENA FAULTY AND SHOT

ME...COLONEL CORNBELT LEADER OF THE ENTIRE FREE WORLD...

I'D HAVE TO CHANGE MY RANK, FOR ONE THING...

TELEPHONE MESSAGE, COLONEL!

DON'T BOTHER ME NOW! I'M FORMULATING STRATEGY!

IT'S ANDRÉ THE HYENA, SIR! HE'S CALLING FROM A PAY PHONE IN BARCELONA!

ANDRÉ?! LET ME TALK TO THAT SON OF A BITCH!

IT IS NOW A FEW MONTHS LATER. WE FIND OURSELVES IN THE WIDE-OPEN AND LAWLESS AFRICAN PORT TOWN OF **DOOWADDHI.**

A MOTOR YACHT APPROACHES. IT IS OUR OLD ACQUAINTANCES THE MODERN-DAY PIRATES OF THE CARIBBEAN AND THEIR CAPTIVE DECK-HAND FREEWHEELIN FRANKLIN.

ALL RIGHT, MEN, **JUST BECAUSE** IT'S YOUR **FIRST SHORE LEAVE** SINCE WE CROSSED THE **ATLANTIC,** DON'T BE **MISBEHAVING** YOURSELVES!

HOLD ON THERE, PROFESSOR! YOU'RE STAYING WITH ME!

WHAT DO YOU WANT TO DO, CAP'N? HOW ABOUT TAKING IN A SEMI-NICE RESTAURANT?

NAW! SHIP'S FOOD IS GOOD ENOUGH FOR A PROFESSIONAL PIRATE LIKE MYSELF! WHAT I GOT IN MIND IS MORE ENTERTAINING!

ER, UH, LOOK! THERE'S AN ARCADE GAME IN THAT **COFFEE SHOP!**

SHUT UP AND FOLLOW ME!

IN HERE!

WHAT IS THIS, SOME KIND OF **MARKET?**

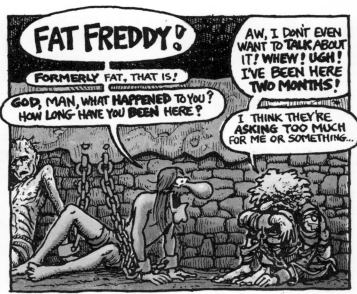

MY GUESS IS WE'LL BE BOUGHT BY SOME FAT, GREASY, S.O.B. LIKE THAT ONE COMING IN THE DOOR!

I HEARD THAT REMARK!

سمين ومشحم في الحقيقة! يا دلال، ماثمن ابني الشيطان كثيري الكلام ضد الحائط؟

SOLD FOR SEVENTEEN MILLION NEW UNITS TO THE OBESE, OLEAGINOUS GENTLEMAN IN THE YELLOW PALANQUIN!

THERE'S NOTHING TO BE ALARMED ABOUT! IT'S ME! YOUR OLD ROOMMATE PHINEAS!

I WAS PRETTY **ANXIOUS** WHEN I FOUND MYSELF **DUMPED** ON THE **RUNWAY** IN THE HOLY CITY OF **MECCA**!

THERE WAS **NOTHING** I COULD **DO** BUT ATTEMPT TO GET MYSELF THROUGH THE FORMIDABLE **CUSTOMS GATE**.

JUST BEFORE I GOT TO THE **INSPECTION** AREA, I SPOTTED A **TELEPHONE** IN AN **ALCOVE** IN THE CORRIDOR.

FORTUNATELY, I HAD BROUGHT ALONG MY **PICOCOMPUTER** AND A HANDY **UNIVERSAL TELEPHONE ACCESS MODEM**.

SIDESTEPPING INTO THE HIDDEN CORNER, I QUICKLY WENT THROUGH A NUMBER OF **LIKELY ACCESS PROCEDURES**.

CLICK CLICK CLICK CLICK CLICK CLICK CLICK

ON THE **SEVENTH TRY** I GOT A **LUCKY HIT** AND GOT **ENTRY** INTO THE **INTERNATIONAL PASSPORT AND CUSTOMS SYSTEM**.

DING

BY THE TIME I REACHED THE **AGENTS** MY **RECORD** HAD BEEN **SUCCESSFULLY ALTERED** FOR THE OCCASION.

A **MACHINE** PROCESSED MY **PASSPORT**, AND THEY NEVER GAVE ME A **SECOND GLANCE** AS I WENT THROUGH THE GATE.

O.K

GLIDE

NOW I WAS OFFICIALLY A **MOSLEM**, AMONG OTHER THINGS. I USED THE **PICOCOMPUTER** AGAIN TO **BOOK A SUITE** AT THE **HOTEL**.

TAXI

FROM MY **ROOM TELEPHONE** IT WAS RELATIVELY **EASY** TO TAP INTO THE COMPUTER SYSTEM OF THE **OIL MINISTRY**.

I WAS GETTING A **PENNY** ON EVERY BARREL OF OIL **MOVED** FOR OVER **THREE** HOURS BEFORE THEY GOT **SUSPICIOUS**!

DING! DING! DING! DING!

THEY HAD **NO IDEA** WHERE THEIR **LEAK** WAS, AND SINCE WHAT I HAD DONE WAS NOT COVERED BY THE **LAW** AT THE TIME, THEY NEVER **LOOKED** TOO **HARD** FOR ME!

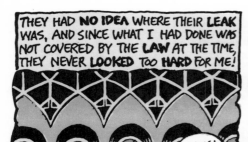

? ♪ DING! DING! DING! DING! ♪

I DECIDED TO **ESTABLISH** THIS **MAIL-ORDER RELIGION** AS A WAY TO **LAUNDER** THE **MONEY** I'D GOT! I NAMED IT "**FUNDALIGIONISM**"!

♪ IT SOUNDS LIKE FUN... ♪ IT HAS A **FUND**... IT'S GOT THAT OLD-TIME 'LIGION... ♪

IT WAS TO BE A **MIXTURE** OF **EVERYTHING** — ISLAM, JUDAISM, CHRISTIANITY, HINDUISM, BUDDHISM, ANIMALISM, CAPITALISM, COMMUNISM, SUN WORSHIP... YOU NAME IT!

I **COBBLED** UP A FEW SIMPLE **TELEVISION ADS** USING THE **VIDEO EQUIPMENT** I HAD CARRIED WITH ME... AND THIS RIDICULOUS **COSTUME** I MADE FROM THE **CURTAINS**!

HI, FOLKS, IT'S ME, FATHER PHINEAS, THE **HONEST HIEROPHANT**, THE **HIGH APOSTLE** OF THE **CHURCH** OF **FUNDALIGION**, COMING TO YOU **LIVE** FROM THE BEAUTIFUL AL'IDDEYINN HOTEL IN DOWNTOWN MECCA...

THEN, USING MY **COMPUTER DICTIONARY**, I TRANSLATED THE TAPES INTO **THREE HUNDRED** OF THE WORLD'S MOST **POPULAR LANGUAGES** AND MAILED THEM TO THE APPROPRIATE **TELEVISION** STATIONS...

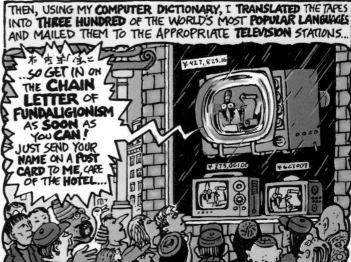

...SO GET IN ON THE **CHAIN LETTER** OF **FUNDALIGIONISM** AS **SOON** AS YOU **CAN**! JUST SEND YOUR NAME ON A POST CARD TO ME, CARE OF THE HOTEL...

I NEVER EXPECTED IT TO BE THE **SUCCESS** THAT IT WAS. FUNDALIGIONISM SEEMED TO STRIKE A **WIDELY RESPONSIVE CHORD**.

YOUR MAIL, SIR!

THANK YOU! JUST PUT IT ON THE COFFEE TABLE!

WITHIN A SHORT PERIOD OF TIME I WAS TAKING IN LITERALLY **BILLIONS** OF **DOLLARS** A WEEK!

FUNDALIGION ENTERPRISES INCORPORATED

RELENTLESSLY THEY ARE FORCE-TAUGHT A CURRICULUM OF PHILOSOPHY, POETRY, RELIGIONS, HISTORY, LITERATURE, GEOLOGY, BIOLOGY, CHEMISTRY, PHYSICS, ASTRONOMY, AGRICULTURE AND MEDICINE.

THEIR BRAINS ARE FED WITH THE WORDS AND THOUGHTS OF CONFUCIUS AND MOHAMMHED, PLATO AND ARISTOTLE, VIRGIL AND DANTE, NEWTON AND DESCARTES, CHAUCER, SHAKESPEARE, SWIFT, NIETZSCHE MARX, EINSTEIN AND SARTRE.

ALSO:

SENECA · MACHIAVELLI · THE BUDDHA · BACON · SPINOZA

SCHOPENHAUER · VOLTAIRE · JEFFERSON · LEIBNIZ · WM. JAMES

NOT TO MENTION: AND OF COURSE...

PYTHAGORAS · ERASMUS · ROUSSEAU · GANDHI · PHINEAS

THEY ARE TAUGHT ALL THE IMPORTANT LANGUAGES OF THE WORLD, INCLUDING (BESIDES ENGLISH) CHINESE, HEBREW, GREEK, LATIN, FRENCH, GERMAN, SPANISH, PORTUGUESE, JAPANESE, RUSSIAN, ITALIAN, DUTCH, DANISH, HINDI & ARABIC.

YOU MUST ALSO BE FAMILIAR WITH THE ANCIENT LANGUAGES, SANSKRIT AND EGYPTIAN, AS SOURCES OF OUR OWN CULTURE! AND LANGUE D'OC AND GAELIC TO GUIDE US THROUGH THE MIDDLE AGES!

IT IS ALSO NECESSARY TO LEARN THE REST OF THE SCANDANAVIAN LANGUAGES, SWEDISH, NORWEGIAN, AND ICELANDIC, AS WELL AS THE FINNISH TONGUE AND ITS ONLY EUROPEAN RELATIVE, HUNGARIAN!

OTHER CRUCIAL LANGUAGES INCLUDE URDU, SINDHI, PUNJABI, BENGALI, PUSHTU, FARSI, VIETNAMESE, RUMANIAN, POLISH, THAI, SLOVENIAN, TURKISH, CATALAN, CZECH, CAMBODIAN, BULGARIAN, BURMESE AND POLYNESIAN!

AND THERE'S NO IGNORING TAGALOG, SERBO-CROATIAN, ARMENIAN, ALBANIAN, KOREAN, MALAY, LAOTIAN, BASQUE, WELSH, KURDISH, NEPALESE, MALTESE, LAPP, MONGOLIAN, INUIT, TIBETAN, NAVAJO, RUMANSCH, LATVIAN, BRETON, LITHUANIAN & FRISIAN!

YOU WILL NEED TO KNOW SWAHILI AND THE AFRICAN LANGUAGES MINA, MASSA, AMHARIC, SETSWANA, SOMALI, SANGO, SONGHAI, MALAGASY, IBO, BANTU, LINGALA AND DAGBANI, NOT TO MENTION AFRIKAANS, YIDDISH AND PIDGIN, PLUS THE UNIVERSAL ESPERANTO!

THEN THERE'S DZONGKHA AND KIKUYU AND YAQUI AND CHICHEWA AND FANTI AND EWE AND CHIPPEWA AND FANG AND BUBI AND TWI AND GA AND BALUCHI AND MAYAN AND BASSA AND EWONDO AND BAHASA AND SINDEBELE AND OUDDAI AND KABYE AND GORANE AND ORIYA AND ISHILUBA AND COTOCOLI AND...

THEY LEARN MATHEMATICS AND CALCULUS, ENGINEERING AND DESIGN, COMPUTER SKILLS, LOGIC, RHETORIC, GRAMMAR AND LINGUISTICS, CIPHERING, CRYPTOLOGY AND PUBLIC RELATIONS.

SPORTS ARE NOT NEGLECTED: INCLUDED IN THE ACADEMIC SCHEDULE ARE EQUESTRIAN SKILLS, SAILING, SCUBADIVING, MOUNTAIN CLIMBING, FLYING, MOTORCYCLE ICE-RACING, AND MARTIAL ARTS.

EQUESTRIAN? IT MEANS "ON HORSEBACK"!
OHH!

...AND MORE MARTIAL ARTS.

TO INSURE THAT THEIR CHARACTERS WILL BE WELL-ROUNDED THEY ALSO TAKE LESSONS IN MUSIC, ART, DANCE, AND DRAMA, AS WELL AS COOKING CLASSES, FOLLOWED BY COURSES IN WINE APPRECIATION AND ORCHID GROWING.

THE PENULTIMATE ACADEMIC DISCIPLINE IS GOVERNMENT/ECONOMICS.

THE GOVERNMENT IS CONTROLLED BY THE EXECUTIVE COMMITTEE OF THE MILITARY JUNTA WITH THE CO-OPERATION OF THEIR EXPERT LEGAL STAFF! IN THESE TIMES OF WORLD PEACE, THE PRINCIPAL FUNCTION OF THE GOVERNMENT IS TO CONTROL THE WORLD'S ECONOMIC AFFAIRS! THIS IS DONE BY MANIPULATING THE VALUE OF THE **NEW UNIT!** SUPPORT IS EFFECTED SO BUSINESS PROSPERITY CAN BE ASSURED FOR THOSE WHO CO-OPERATE WITH THE GOVERNMENT!

ER, AM I CORRECT, COLONEL?

OF COURSE THERE ARE ALSO SPECIAL FAVORS FOR THE VERY RICH, SUCH AS FATHER PHINEAS!

NOW TO OUR LAST CLASS! IT'S CALLED "CITIZENSHIP"!

IT'S BEING TAUGHT BY... PHINEAS! HIMSELF!

AS A **WORLD CITIZEN**, ONE WILL BE REQUIRED TO UNDERSTAND HOW THE WORLD GOVERNMENT FUNCTIONS, IN THE UNLIKELY EVENT ONE IS EVER CALLED UPON TO TAKE PART IN A **VOTE**.

A SHORT TIME AGO (YOU MAY HAVE MISSED THIS WHILE YOU WERE IN THE SLAVE MARKET) **MARTIAL LAW** WAS DECLARED EVERYWHERE IN RESPONSE TO A VAGUE WORLDWIDE **TERRORIST THREAT**, WHICH BROUGHT INTO POWER A CERTAIN COLONEL H. (FOR HAMMERLOCK) CORNBELT AS CHAIRMAN OF A GIGANTIC COMMITTEE OF COLONELS, WITH CIVIL MATTERS BEING HANDLED BY THE MYSTERIOUS ATTORNEY GENERAL AND SUPREME COURT JUSTICE, ANDREW L. HYENA.

THERE WAS A **TOTAL NEWS BLACKOUT**. IT IS SPECULATED THAT THE NUMEROUS CIVILIAN GOVERNMENTS AND THE MEMBERS OF THE MILITARY ABOVE THE RANK OF COLONEL WERE GIVEN THEIR CHOICE BETWEEN **VOLUNTARY RETIREMENT** OR BEING SOLD INTO THE **SLAVE MARKET**. NOW THERE'S NO MORE WAR, NO MORE **REGIONAL CONFLICTS**, AND NO MORE **UNEMPLOYMENT**. NOR ARE THERE ANY **INDEPENDENT NEWSPAPERS**. FATHER PHINEAS IS THE ONLY THING ANYONE CAN GET ON **TELEVISION**. IT'S BEEN RATHER A **WINDFALL** FOR **FUNDALIGIONISM**, I MUST SAY.

NEXT SLIDE, PLEASE.

EVERYWHERE AT PRESENT ONE SEES LARGE NUMBERS OF PEACEFUL **GOVERNMENT EMPLOYEES**. ALMOST ALL CITIZENS ARE EMPLOYED BY THE GOVERNMENT. ANY PERSON WHO DOES **NOT** ALREADY HAVE A JOB WILL BE **GIVEN** ONE BY THE GOVERNMENT. (THAT OF POLICEMAN, IF ONE IS **LUCKY**). THE MORE **DIFFICULT** OF THE LAW ENFORCEMENT TASKS ARE HANDLED BY THE NEW ERA **SHOCK TROOPS** UNDER THE **DIRECT ORDERS** OF THE EXECUTIVE **COMMITTEE** OF THE NEW ERA WORLD GOVERNMENT.

THE TOP LEVELS OF GOVERNMENT ARE LOCATED IN A REMOTE, INVINCIBLE UNDERGROUND BUNKER WITH STORED SUPPLIES TO LAST **DECADES**. MISSILES ARE **EVERYWHERE**, POINTING IN **ALL** DIRECTIONS. ANY SORT OF **DISTURBANCE**, EVEN A **LOUD NOISE**, COULD CAUSE **THOUSANDS** OF THEM TO BE **LAUNCHED**.

THAT IS WHY **ELECTRIC ROCK AND ROLL MUSIC** IS NO LONGER ALLOWED.

EXCEPT ON THE **FATHER PHINEAS** SHOW.

HALLELUJAHGOBBLE! HALLELUJAHGOBBLE!

CLASS DISMISSED.

FINAL EXAMINATIONS ARE A VERY SERIOUS EVENT IN NEW ERA CULTURE.

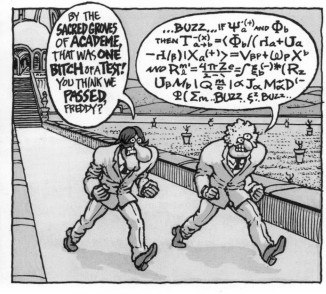

BY THE SACRED GROVES OF ACADEME, THAT WAS **ONE BITCH OF A TEST!** YOU THINK WE **PASSED**, FREDDY?

$...BUZZ... IF \Psi_a'^{(+)}$ AND Φ_b THEN $T_{a \to b}^{-(x)} = \langle \Phi_b | (r_a + U_a - r_{a/\beta}) | X_a^{(+)} \rangle = V_{\beta P} + \omega_P X^b$ AND $R_\ell^{m_i} = \frac{4\pi Z e}{2-x} = \int_{\mathcal{E}_b}^{(-)*} (R_z U_\beta M_b | Q \frac{m}{\mathcal{E}} | \alpha J_\alpha M \bar{x} D'^{-} \Phi (\sum m ... BUZZ... \xi^2 ... BUZZ...$

MEANWHILE, IN THE NEW ERA WORLD GOVERNMENT COMMAND BUNKER ON ROCKALL ISLAND IN THE NORTH ATLANTIC, THINGS ARE NOT PROCEEDING AS SMOOTHLY AS HAD BEEN ANTICIPATED.

ATTENTION! COLONEL CORNBELT APPROACHES!

PSST! MR. LE HYENA! STAND UP! HE'S COMING!

I DON'T HAVE TO STAND UP! HE'S NOT **MY** SUPERIOR!

AT EASE, MEN! (AHEM) TODAY'S SESSION OF THE EXECUTIVE COMMITTEE OF THE NEW ERA WORLD GOVERNMENT WILL NOW OFFICIALLY COMMENCE!

AM I IN **ORDER**, ANDR... UH, **MR. LE HYENA**?

PROCEED, COLONEL!

THE FIRST ITEM ON THE AGENDA IS THE PROPOSED PROMOTION IN RANK FOR OUR ESTEEMED LEADER, COL. CORNBELT!

OUT OF THE QUESTION!

IT'S JUST THAT THE TERM "COLONEL" SEEMS TO LACK SUFFICIENT WEIGHT FOR THE **OFFICE**!

PERHAPS YOU'VE **FORGOTTEN**, COLONEL CORNBELT, THAT THE WAY YOU **CAME TO POWER** IN THE **FIRST** PLACE WAS THROUGH THE LEGISLATIVE **OUTLAWING OF ALL** RANKS **ABOVE** THAT OF COLONEL!

WHY DON'T YOU JUST CALL YOURSELF "COLONEL-TO-THE TWELFTH POWER" OR SOMETHING LIKE THAT? COLONEL'² CORNBELT!

HA HA!

HA HA HA!

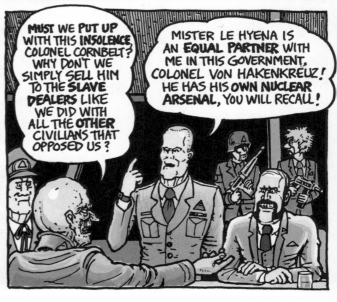

MUST WE PUT UP WITH THIS INSOLENCE COLONEL CORNBELT? WHY DON'T WE SIMPLY SELL HIM TO THE **SLAVE DEALERS** LIKE WE DID WITH ALL THE **OTHER** CIVILIANS THAT OPPOSED US?

MISTER LE HYENA IS AN **EQUAL PARTNER** WITH ME IN THIS GOVERNMENT, COLONEL VON HAKENKREUZ! HE HAS HIS **OWN** NUCLEAR ARSENAL, YOU WILL RECALL!

...BUT I'M SO BUSY... OH, VERY WELL, BUT THESE ARE MY CONDITIONS, COLONEL... OKAY, I'LL BE THERE AS SOON AS POSSIBLE...

(SOUNDS LIKE HE'S BEING CALLED AWAY!)

(GOOD!)

ANOTHER CEREMONIAL HONOR... THEY'RE APPOINTING ME TO A POSITION IN THE GOVERNMENT. MY TITLE WILL BE "EMPEROR OF EARTH."

(SIGH) WHAT DOES THE TITLE OF EMPEROR MEAN TO ME? I'M ALREADY THE RICHEST MAN ON EARTH AND HEAD OF THE CHURCH OF FUNDALIGIONISM.

...BUT THE CORONATION IS TO BE ONE MONTH FROM TODAY. I'M TRANSFERRING YOU TO MY PERSONAL STAFF TO BE IN CHARGE OF ARRANGING THE CEREMONY. THEY'VE ALREADY CHOSEN THE SITE. IT'S ON THE NORTH SHORE OF LOCH NESS IN SCOTLAND.

LET'S SEE... WE'LL NEED A TWO HUNDRED FOOT HIGH MAIN GRANDSTAND FACING THE LAKE... A LARGE REVIEWING STAND AND LECTURN... THEATRICAL LIGHTING... AN IMMENSELY POWERFUL PUBLIC ADDRESS SYSTEM... A LARGE STONE STATUE OF ME...

YOU, FRANKLIN, WILL BE DRESSED IN THE CEREMONIAL YELLOW AND GREEN POLKA-DOT VELOUR ROBES OF THE SACRED PERSONAL ASSISTANTS OF FATHER PHINEAS, AND YOU, FREDDY, WILL BE WEARING THE VENERATED PINK SILK SKIRTS OF THE ZOUAVES OF FUNDALIGIONISM.

THAT NIGHT WHILE PHINEAS IS DOING HIS REGULAR FOUR-HOUR SHOW, FRANKLIN AND FREDDY ESCAPE.

WE'RE GOING TO HAVE TO BREAK UP THIS LITTLE PARTY!

I'VE LEARNED HOW TO ENDURE JUST ABOUT ANYTHING, BUT PHINEAS EMPEROR OF EARTH IS JUST TOO MUCH!

OUTSIDE PHINEAS' STRONGLY-PROTECTED CHATEAU, DISASTER STRIKES IMMEDIATELY.

TRAVELING ON FOOT AT NIGHT, FRANKLIN AND FREDDY REACH CAIRO IN A WEEK. IN ORDER TO OBTAIN WATER THEY BRIBE GOVERNMENT OFFICIALS

IN TEL AVIV, THERE ARE FOOD RIOTS AND ENORMOUS SWARMS OF REFUGEES. HERE THEY SEE THEIR FIRST OF MANY FUNDALIGIONIST PILGRIMS ON THEIR WAY TO THE CORONATION.

A FOURTEEN-SIDED CIVIL WAR STILL RAGES IN BEIRUT, NEW ERA OR NOT.

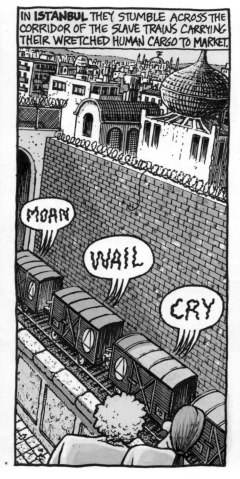

IN ISTANBUL THEY STUMBLE ACROSS THE CORRIDOR OF THE SLAVE TRAINS CARRYING THEIR WRETCHED HUMAN CARGO TO MARKET.

THE CLASSIC RUINS OF ATHENS HAVE BEEN TRANSFORMED INTO A TELEVISION STUDIO AND RALLYING POINT FOR FUNDALIGIONIST PILGRIMS WHOSE HORDES NOW CLOG THE HIGHWAYS.

TO GET TO **VENICE** THEY MUST TRAVEL BY SMALL BOAT ALONG THE COAST AT NIGHT.

THE POLICE ARE INTERROGATING THE CITIZENS OF **MARSEILLES**, ONE BY ONE. IT IS NO PLACE TO BE HANGING AROUND.

THE MOUNTAIN PASSES OF THE PYRENEES ARE PATROLLED BY THE DREADED **GUARDIA CIVIL** AS THE TWO FREAK BROTHERS NEAR THEIR DESTINATION, THE CITY OF **BARCELONA**.

IN BARCELONA THEY SEEK OUT **PABLO PEGASO**.

NEVER MADE IT TO **BOGOTA**, EH?

WELL, COME IN!

OVER A SUPERBLY-PREPARED MEAL THEY ENJOY LEISURELY CONVERSATION.

THIS IS THE NICEST **LAFITE-ROTHSCHILD** I'VE HAD IN SOME TIME!

'98 OR '99, I'D GUESS!

YOU SEEM TO BE **WELL-INSULATED** FROM THE **OUTSIDE WORLD** HERE IN THIS **MANSION**, MR. PEGASO!

PHOOEY! STONE WALLS A MERE METER IN THICKNESS WON'T DO ANYBODY ANY GOOD WHEN THE **REAL FIGHTING** BREAKS OUT!

I'M NOT WORRIED BY A FEW **THUGS** OUT ON THE **STREETS!** BUT IF THAT STUPID BUNCH OF FASCISTS IN THE GOVERNMENT KEEPS ON, THERE ARE GOING TO BE **NUCLEAR WEAPONS** GOING OFF **ALL OVER** THE DAMN PLACE!

EVERYONE KNOWS THESE RELATIVELY 'PEACEFUL' TIMES AREN'T GOING TO LAST FOREVER! LET ME SHOW YOU MY **LATEST INVENTION**— A SYSTEM TO MAKE MYSELF **ENTIRELY INDEPENDENT** OF THE NORMAL **FOOD SUPPLY** CHAIN!

TAKE A LOOK AT **THIS!**

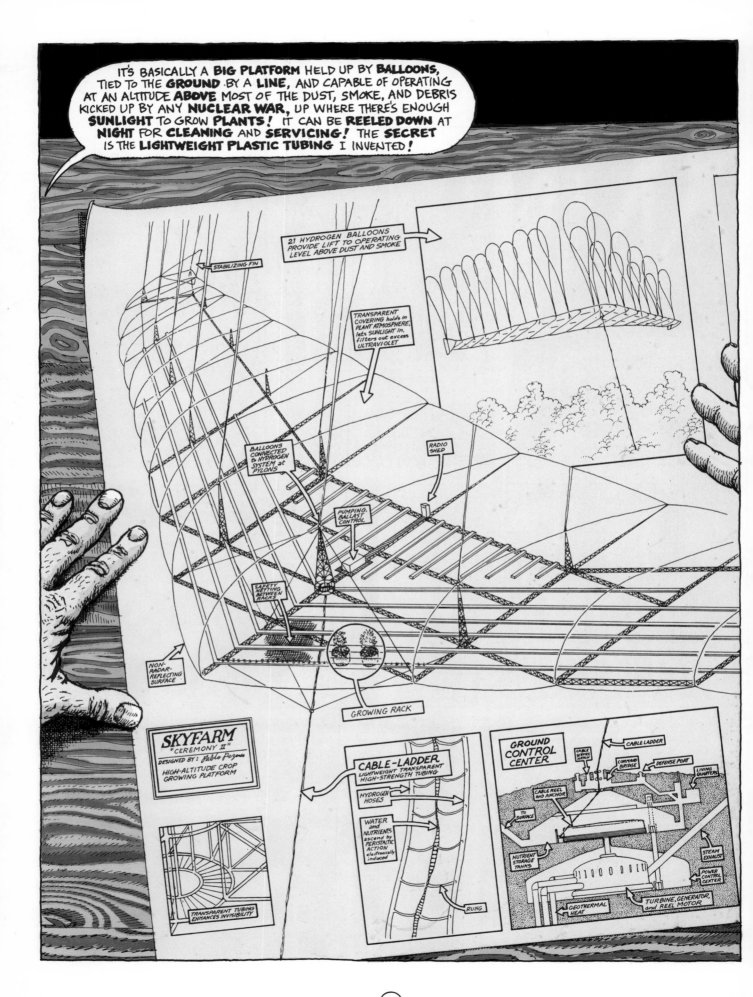

MINGLING WITH THE SWARMS OF FUNDALIGIONIST PILGRIMS, OUR HEROS MAKE THEIR WAY TO LOCH NESS.

GOSH, I'LL BE SO HAPPY TO SEE PHINEAS! HOW ABOUT YOU, BROTHER?

THEY ARRIVE JUST BEFORE DAWN ON THE DAY OF THE CORONATION.

THERE'S THE CEREMONIAL PLATFORM, ACROSS THE LAKE!

THEY'VE BUILT A HUGE ELECTRIC FENCE TO KEEP THE PILGRIMS OVER ON THIS SIDE!

THIS'LL BE NO PROBLEM AT ALL! GIVE ME THE CUTTING TORCH!

ACROSS THE LAKE IN THE SECURE AREA, PHINEAS HAS JUST ARRIVED TO DISCUSS THE FINAL DETAILS OF THE CEREMONY, AND HE IS DISCOVERING THAT BEING EMPEROR MIGHT NOT BE EXACTLY LIKE HE HAD ENVISIONED.

WE LET YOU CHOOSE YOUR OWN TITLE, SO YOU'LL BE "EMPEROR," BUT YOU'RE ONLY THE FIGUREHEAD FOR THE NEW ERA! YOU'LL BE EXPECTED TO FOLLOW OUR SUGGESTIONS!

I'LL DO AS I WISH! I'M THE RICHEST MAN IN THE WORLD!

TODAY YOU'RE THE RICHEST, BUT TOMORROW, WHO KNOWS? MY MEN CONTROL THE VALUE OF YOUR CURRENCY!

(IF YOU SIDE AGAINST ME, YOU CAN EXPECT A BULLET IN THE BACK OF YOUR HEAD!)

FRANKLIN AND FREDDY CROSS THE LAKE.

HMMM... I KEEP THINKING I'VE SEEN THIS PLACE SOMEWHERE BEFORE!

AYEEEEE! YARRRGH!

(FOR GOD'S SAKE, FREDDY, BE QUIET! WHAT'S THE MATTER?)

(LOCH NESS MONSTER!)

(DOZENS OF 'EM!)

(THEY'RE ONLY ABOUT ONE INCH LONG, BUT THEY'RE ICKY AS HELL.)

(WHAT'S THAT THING?)

(IT'S ANDRÉ'S PORTABLE NUCLEAR BOMB! I HID IT HERE WHEN I WAS RUNNING AWAY FROM HIM, MORE THAN SIX MONTHS AGO!)

IT IS NOON. PHINEAS HAS ASCENDED THE STAGE, FLANKED BY COLONEL CORNBELT AND ANDRÉ THE HYENA. A GIGANTIC MUSICAL FANFARE CLIMAXES AND FADES AWAY.

THEN A VAST SILENCE FALLS.

SUDDENLY, BEFORE THE CROWN CAN BE PLACED ON HIS HEAD, PHINEAS GRABS A MIKE.

FRIENDS, FAITHFUL FOLLOWERS OF FUNDALIGIONISM, AND ADHERENTS OF THE NEW ERA WORLD GOVERNMENT... LISTEN TO ME... I WANT TO TELL YOU SOMETHING, EVEN IF IT'S TOO LATE!

HEY, WHAT'RE YOU DOING?

STICK TO THE SCRIPT!

THROUGH THE FIVE-HUNDRED-THOUSAND WATT PUBLIC ADDRESS SYSTEM, HIS VOICE CAN BE HEARD THE LENGTH AND BREADTH OF THE LAKE.

COLONEL CORNBELT AND ANDRÉ LE HYENA HAVE TRIED TO PERSUADE ME TO SUPPORT THEIR NEW ERA COALITION GOVERNMENT, BUT I AM REFUSING THEIR REQUEST!

QUICK! PULL HIS PLUG!

DON'T ORDER ME AROUND! PULL IT YOURSELF!

BENEATH THE GRANDSTAND...

THESE MILITARISTS AND TERRORISTS ARE THE SCUM OF HUMANITY AND THE SCOURGE OF THE EARTH! SOMEONE HAS TO SAY NO TO THEM! THERE'S ONLY ONE TYPE OF PERSON THAT'S MORE DANGEROUS THAN THESE AUTHORITARIAN THUGS...

HEY, NOT BAD!

MAYBE WE WON'T HAVE TO KILL HIM AFTER ALL!

...AND THAT'S A RANTING RELIGIOUS DEMAGOGUE WHO TAKES ADVANTAGE OF THE NATURAL STUPIDITY OF ORDINARY, NICE PEOPLE AND THEIR SUPERSTITIONS IN ORDER TO MAKE A LOT OF MONEY AND FURTHER HIS OWN SELFISH AIMS AND THE AIMS OF A BUNCH OF POWER-HUNGRY FASCISTS AND HIGH-TECH TERRORISTS WHO WANT TO IMPOSE THEIR TOTALITARIAN TYRANNY ON EVERYONE AND HOLD PEOPLE IN SLAVERY EVEN IF IT IS FOR THE SLAVE'S OWN BENEFIT!

MY WILL WAS DOMINATED BY GREED, BUT NOW I'M THE POOREST PERSON ON EARTH BECAUSE I'VE LOST MY TWO BEST FRIENDS! I DON'T EVEN LIKE MONEY! I'M JUST A POOR OLD HIPPIE!

LET THIS BE A LESSON IN HUMILITY TO US ALL!

ON THE FAR BANK THE MULTITUDES STAND AGAPE AT THEIR VIDEO MONITORS.

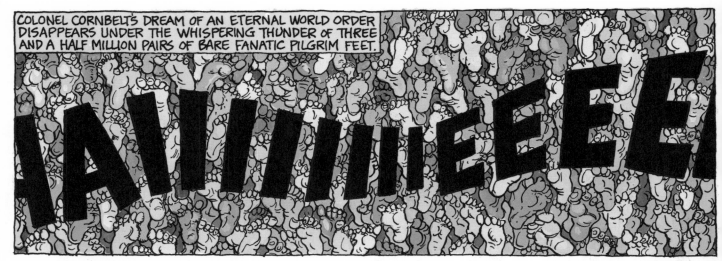

COLONEL CORNBELT'S DREAM OF AN ETERNAL WORLD ORDER DISAPPEARS UNDER THE WHISPERING THUNDER OF THREE AND A HALF MILLION PAIRS OF BARE FANATIC PILGRIM FEET.

IN THE CONFUSION, THE FREAK BROTHERS MAKE IT TO PHINEA'S PRIVATE AIRPLANE.

THEY TAKE OFF IN A HAIL OF FIRE.

RADAR INDICATES NO PURSUIT.

AIRSPEED FIFTEEN SEVEN SIX FOUR NINER.

YOU GUYS WANT TO GET HIGH? TRY SOME OF MY IMPERIAL STASH!

A FEW HOURS LATER...

WE'RE OVER THE CO-ORDINATES NOW, I THINK, IF I REMEMBER HOW TO USE THIS STUPID COMPUTER CORRECTLY!

FOR SOME REASON I CAN'T RECALL HOW TO LAND THIS PARTICULAR TYPE OF AIRCRAFT! WE'RE GOING TO HAVE TO BAIL OUT!

IT'LL PROBABLY CRASH HARMLESSLY OUT IN THE PACIFIC SOMEWHERE!

THEIR LANDING POINT IS A JUNGLE-CHOKED VOLCANIC CRATER CONCEALING A NUMBER OF MODERN BUILDINGS AND A SMALL AIRSTRIP.

THIS MUST BE THE GROUND SUPPORT SYSTEM FOR PABLO PEGASO'S SKYFARM!

IT'S THAT COLONY OF SURVIVALISTS I MET EARLIER!

WELCOME! ALLOW ME TO INTRODUCE MY DAUGHTER PIGI!

I SEE YOU'VE BROUGHT THE FAMOUS FATHER PHINEAS WITH YOU! DID YOU MANAGE TO DISRUPT THE CORONATION?

YOU BET WE DID! THEY WERE ALL SHOOTING AT ONE ANOTHER WHEN WE MADE OUR ESCAPE!

I BELIEVE WE'VE MET!

HAVE WE?

DO YOU STILL HAVE JOBS FOR US?

YES, I WANT YOU TO BE THE VEHICLE CREW, SO I CAN KEEP THESE SURLY INDIANS DOWN ON THE GROUND WHERE I CAN WATCH 'EM!

YOUR JOB WILL BE TO REEL THE PLATFORM DOWN AT NIGHT, CLIMB UP THE CABLE LADDER, AND PERFORM ROUTINE MAINTENANCE WORK LIKE BALLAST-BALANCING AND CROP HARVESTING!

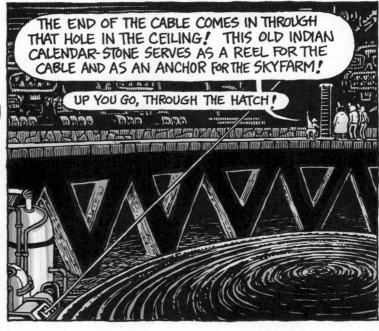

THE END OF THE CABLE COMES IN THROUGH THAT HOLE IN THE CEILING! THIS OLD INDIAN CALENDAR-STONE SERVES AS A REEL FOR THE CABLE AND AS AN ANCHOR FOR THE SKYFARM!

UP YOU GO, THROUGH THE HATCH!

THE FREAK BROTHERS ADAPT QUICKLY TO THIS AGRICULTURAL MODE OF LIFE.

BEFORE MANY DAYS, THEY HAVE PLANTED MARIJUANA BETWEEN THE ROWS OF CORN.

THEY ARE SOON SPENDING ALL THEIR NIGHT HOURS ALOFT, SMOKING UP THEIR CROPS.

ONE DAY FAT FREDDY TRADES THE BOMB TO ONE OF THE INDIANS FOR A PACK OF COLORED ROLLING PAPERS.

NOT TOO MANY DAYS LATER, THE FREAK BROTHERS ACCIDENTALLY LEAVE SO MUCH SMOKE IN THE SKYFARM FROM THEIR ALL-NIGHT SMOKING SESSION THAT THE PLATFORM BECOMES VISIBLE TO AN OBSERVER ON THE GROUND.

WHAT'S THE MATTER **NOW**, CADET-COLONEL PICHON? YOU HAVEN'T SPOTTED **ANDRÉ**, HAVE YOU?

COLONEL CORNBELT, SIR!

IT'S A **U.F.O.**, SIR!

THE COLONELS ARE SOON ON THEIR WAY OVERLAND TO THE GROUND CONTROL CENTER, FORTY MILES FROM THEIR POST.

IT'S SOME SORT OF HUGE **PLATFORM** HELD UP BY TRANSPARENT **BALLOONS**! I THINK I SEE **FOLIAGE** IN THERE!

THAT DEVICE WOULD HAVE TREMENDOUS POTENTIAL AS A **SURVIVAL STATION** IN THE EVENT OF **NUCLEAR WAR**! IT'S JUST WHAT WE **NEED**!

IT IS ALMOST DARK WHEN THEY ARRIVE AT THE CRATER.

THERE ARE A BUNCH OF **TRANSPARENT CABLES** COMING DOWN FROM IT, GOING INTO THAT **HOLE** IN THE GROUND!

IT'S THEIR **BASE**! FAN OUT AND ENCIRCLE THE AREA!

COME OUT WITH YOUR HANDS ABOVE YOUR HEADS!

WHO IS IT?

IT'S A RATTY-LOOKING GROUP OF GUYS IN **MILITARY** UNIFORMS!

GOOD LORD! IT'S **COLONEL CORNBELT** AND HIS MEN!

THEY HAVE US **SURROUNDED**! BAR THE DOORS!

IT'S GETTING **DARK**! LISTEN, WE CAN GO UP THE CABLE, CAST **OFF**, AND WITH ANY LUCK AT **ALL** WE'LL BE OVER THE **AMAZON** BASIN BY DAWN!

GOOD IDEA!

REEL IT IN!

WELL, I'M GOING TO STAY IN **HERE** AND HOLD 'EM OFF! THIS PLACE IS **IMPREGNABLE**!

COLONEL CORNBELT AND HIS OFFICERS REACH THE TOP OF THE CABLE-LADDER.

WHERE DID THEY GO?

THEY'RE UP HERE SOMEPLACE! SPREAD OUT AND WE'LL FIND 'EM!

A FEW MINUTES LATER, ANDRÉ AND HIS GANG BOARD THE PLATFORM.

WHERE DID THEY GO?

THEY'RE UP HERE SOMEPLACE! SPREAD OUT AND WE'LL FIND 'EM!

FROM TIME TO TIME A SHOT RINGS OUT IN THE DARKNESS.

I'M NOT GOING TO BE ABLE TO GET THESE HOSES LOOSE!

QUICK, WE GOTTA HIDE!

PABLO AND PIGI PEGASO ESCAPE THROUGH THE JUNGLE ON THEIR MECHANICAL ROADRUNNERS.

THAR SHE BLOWS!

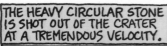

THE HEAVY CIRCULAR STONE IS SHOT OUT OF THE CRATER AT A TREMENDOUS VELOCITY.

POIT!

PABLO PEGASO'S MIRACLE TUBING CONNECTING STONE AND SKYFARM STRETCHES BUT HOLDS.

THE SKYFARM IS PULLED UPWARD, SLOWLY AT FIRST BECAUSE OF THE ANGLE AND STRETCH OF THE CABLE...

...THEN RAPIDLY, TO DISAPPEAR FOREVER INTO THE VAST REACHES OF OUTER SPACE, CARRYING ALL OF THE BAD GUYS WITH IT. *

BYE-BYE, COLONEL KAKOV!

*WITH THE EXCEPTION OF CADET-COLONEL PICHON, WHO WAS TOO STOUT TO ATTEMPT TO CLIMB THE LADDER IN THE FIRST PLACE, AND WHO SURVIVED TO BECOME DICTATOR-FOR-LIFE OF ALL OF CENTRAL AMERICA, BUT THAT IS ANOTHER STORY.

FORTUNATELY, THE FREAK BROTHERS HAD BEEN CARRIED OFF AT THE VERY LAST MOMENT BY SMILIN' MYLAN, FLYING AN ULTRALIGHTWEIGHT FOLDING TWO-PASSENGER AIRCRAFT.

I THOUGHT YOU SAID YOU'D LOST YOUR PILOT'S LICENSE, MYLAN!

DON'T **NEED A** LICENSE TO FLY ONE OF **THESE!**

YEAH! SMILIN' MYLAN! I REMEMBER YOU! I USED TO READ ABOUT YOUR ADVENTURES IN THE **FUNNY PAPERS** WHEN I WAS A LITTLE **BOY!**

YOU WERE A PILOT IN THE **PACIFIC** AGAINST THE **JAPANESE!** DIDN'T YOU FLY A **T6B** AT THE BATTLE OF **MIDWAY** OR SOMETHING LIKE THAT?

NAW, THAT'S MY **GRANDAD** YOU'RE THINKING ABOUT—SMILIN' MYLAN **I!** HE FOUGHT IN WORLD WAR **TWO!** MY **DAD**, SMILIN' MYLAN **II**, FLEW IN **KOREA!** I'M SMILIN' MYLAN **3d!** AND **MY** GIG WAS FLYING **B-52's** IN 'NAM!

YEAH, THAT'S RIGHT! VIET NAM! I'M NOT AS **OLD** AS I **LOOK!** THAT WAR TOOK A **LOT** OUT OF **ALL** OF US!

WE WERE JUST A **HAPPY-GO-LUCKY** BUNCH OF **KIDS**, DRINKING A LOT OF **BOOZE**, SMOKING A LOT OF **GRASS**, SNORTING UP A LOT OF **COKE**...

...DOING A LOT OF **SPEED**, AND **REDS**, AND **OPIUM**... **ANGEL DUST**... YOU **NAME** IT... MY PERSONAL FAVORITE WAS **LSD-25**...

I RECALL ONE DAY I DROPPED TWENTY-FIVE HITS OF "THE **RIGHT STUFF**" JUST BEFORE WE TOOK OFF ON A **BOMB RUN**...

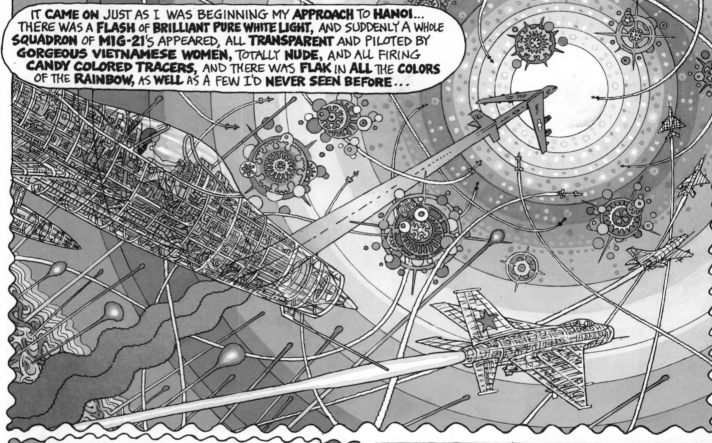

IT CAME **ON** JUST AS I WAS BEGINNING MY **APPROACH** TO **HANOI**... THERE WAS A **FLASH** OF **BRILLIANT PURE WHITE LIGHT**, AND SUDDENLY A WHOLE **SQUADRON** OF **MIG-21**'S APPEARED, ALL **TRANSPARENT** AND PILOTED BY **GORGEOUS VIETNAMESE WOMEN**, TOTALLY **NUDE**, AND ALL FIRING **CANDY COLORED TRACERS**, AND THERE WAS **FLAK** IN **ALL** THE COLORS OF THE **RAINBOW**, AS WELL AS A FEW I'D **NEVER SEEN BEFORE**...

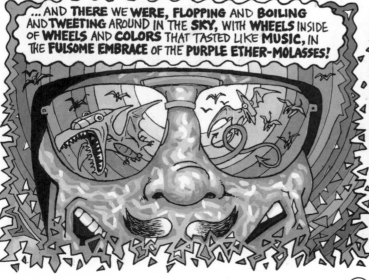

...AND **THERE** WE **WERE**, **FLOPPING** AND **BOILING** AND **TWEETING** AROUND **IN** THE **SKY**, WITH **WHEELS** INSIDE OF **WHEELS** AND **COLORS** THAT TASTED LIKE **MUSIC**, IN THE **FULSOME EMBRACE** OF THE **PURPLE ETHER-MOLASSES!**

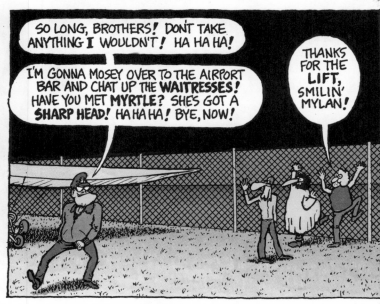

THE END

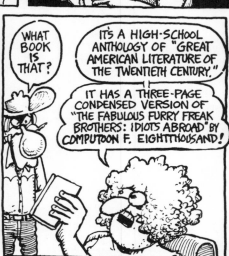

Nature Library of Color
HORSES AND FOALS

CRESCENT

Of the many animals that have befriended man the horse is surely the most magnificent. It is a symbol of strength, courage and majesty. On its sturdy back have sat great warriors, monarchs and statesmen; great conquests have been made and new territory explored. Without it the invention of the wheel would have been virtually redundant and much of the land upon which man grew his own food would have remained uncultivated. It is impossible to imagine just how differently the pattern of our own history would have emerged had it not been for the hard work, patience and loyalty of the horse, and for this contribution alone we are indebted to it. Even today, as its agricultural and haulage uses draw to a close, the horse remains an important part of our society and increases our enjoyment of leisure time as the popularity of equestrian sports grows. It is flattering that such a noble beast is happy to feature so prominently in our society and the place it occupies in many peoples' lives is indispensable.

To look at the stately horse of the modern age it is hard to believe that its ancestor was little bigger than a fox. But skeletons unearthed in the Mississippi Valley in the United States show that the first horse Eohippus, that foraged the undergrowth in the Eocene forests over fifty million years ago, stood roughly one foot high. Eohippus (Greek for the 'Dawn Horse') was unique in that it had four toes on the front limb and only three on the hind, but many scientists believe that it could run as fast as the modern race horse. Its modest frame, however, was

(1) Przewalski's Wild Horse and Foal.
(2) A sleepy Arab foal nuzzles the buttercups and daisies in a sunny meadow.
(3) The stance of this Arab foal emphasises its long, gangling legs. (4) This Arab horse displays a regal turn of the neck. (5) An appealingly fluffy New Forest foal seen on Wiverley Plain, Hampshire, England. (6) Arab mare and foal. (7) Shire foal.

5

6

7

not suitably equipped to survive in its environment and it mysteriously disappeared. But by this time more advanced species had developed. Over millions of years these species constantly underwent change, adapting to their surroundings and developing qualities specifically designed for their survival. Eventually they evolved into Equus, the single species to which all modern horses belong. Early Equus, a sturdy dun-coloured animal now known as Przewalski's horse, travelled outwards from Eurasia establishing local breeds to the east and west. In Europe, breeds were established from the migratory horses which ranged through Asia Minor and they were also to reappear in the New World, in 1519, when the Spanish explorer Hernando Cortez, transported the ancestral horse to its original prehistoric home.

The origins of the domestic horse are less clear. All are descended from four sub-species of the original wild horse but exactly when the horse was first harnessed is not accurately known. Prehistoric man drew pictures of the early horse on the walls of his cave many thousands of years ago but it is unlikely that he did more than keep the herds for meat, milk and hides. The first horsemen were probably the barbarian nomads of Central Asia who rode hardy wild ponies. Certainly by the end of the Bronze Age the horse's potential had been realised and from then until the invention of the steam train in the 19th century, most land transport all over the world was carried out by horseback. On farms and in coalmines the horse proved equally invaluable and it is only recently that the role of the horse has changed from servant to friend. Unfortunately, so well did the horse carry out the work man asked of it that man forgot the horse's body was evolved for its own survival and not specifically for his usage. Instead of being grateful that so noble a beast should allow its skills to be used for the purpose of his own progression,

(1) Przewalski's Wild Horse and foal. (2) Arab mare and foal. (3) Three horses bask in evening sunlight. (4) This peaceful grey is seen in the Carmargue, France. (5) Group of four greys. (6) Grazing in Norway. (7) Pair of Arab fillies. (8) Arab foal. Overleaf Part bred Arab colt and mare.

man frequently abused the horse by overworking it. Luckily, it is, for the most part, on record that the horse endured such treatment and now it enjoys a more comfortable existence.

Horses and Battle

The horse's potential on the battlefield was realised very early on. History relates that the first major victory of cavalry over the infantry was in AD 378 when the Goths defeated the Romans at Adrianople, but even before this horses were used to pull chariots. It was with the invention of javelins and bows that the need to employ the horse elsewhere in battle arose and the cavalry was established, quickly becoming an army's major striking force. By the middle of the sixth century the Great Horse of Europe, which is the ancestor of all the heavy breeds used in war, had grown considerably in size and strength and heavy armour was introduced. When

King John brought over from Europe a hundred dray stallions to combine with the English stock, the size of the horse increased further and battles became considerably more ferocious.

The invention of firearms almost totally displaced the cavalry from the battlefield and today it serves no function in modern warfare. But all over the world small cavalry units are maintained and horses are the main feature of military displays and ceremonial occasions.

(1) Pure bred Arab foal. (2) Arab horse. (3) Pure bred Arab foal seen in Sussex, England. (4) Proud cream mare and pretty foal. (5) Dun Arab mare and foal. (6) These delightful Shetland ponies contentedly munch hay on a snow-dusted hillside in Somerset, England. (7) Piebald Shetland pony. (8) An Arab foal lies at the feet of its protective mother.

1

5

6

2

3

4

Horses and Agriculture

Until the invention of machinery the horse's use in agriculture was indispensable. All farm work was carried out with its help and the transportation of goods was by horseback or horse-and-cart, with the added advantage that the horse was cheap to run – a fact which few modern machines can claim to be.

Man first discovered how invaluable the horse would be in agriculture when he used the wild horse to help him hunt. He quickly realised that if he stayed in one place and kept a few of the animals he hunted in captivity they would breed and he would no longer have to go out searching for his food. He also discovered that he could cultivate the land around him and grow his own crops and for both purposes the horse became an invaluable aid. When cattle strayed it was a simple enough task to round them up if on horseback and when the plough was invented it was eventually the horse that pulled it.

On most large farms throughout the world machines now do the work that was once done by the horse, but few are as versatile, and in many mountainous regions the horse is still the most efficient means of ploughing the land and transporting goods.

Famous Breeds

If the mating of two horses of the same kind consistently results in a horse of the same appearance, colour, height and temperament it can be said that these horses belong to a particular breed. There are numerous modern breeds that vary greatly in appearance and character, but one common feature is that they all developed from the stocky wild horse of central Asia. When and how the emergence of different breeds occurred is unclear, but it is likely that the migratory horses that travelled across Europe and Asia in prehistoric times eventually developed, broadly speaking, into two groups of horses; the hot-blooded Arab-Barbs, typified by the Arabian, and the heavier working breeds.

The Arabian, renowned for its beauty, stamina and spirited yet gentle nature is considered the monarch amongst horses. It moves

(1) Richly caparisoned horses take part in a ploughing championship. (2) Horses still play an important part in the work of many farms. (3) The proud farmer displays his trusty, and strong companion. (4) Working horses can easily be distinguished by their build. (5) Ploughing competition. (6) Ploughing with Shire horses. (7) Beautifully kitted out horse on show. (8), (9) and (10) Hard at work or on display, horses are true friends.

with a grace no other horse can match – its limbs long and slender, its small head held high with an air of superiority. First mentioned in 400 BC it is thought to have stemmed from a gift of five mares given to Muhammed by his followers. It was imported into Europe after the crusades and has remained pure bred until today. It is also the forefather of all modern light breeds. The swiftest of all breeds descended from the Arabian is the Thoroughbred, the favourite in many equestrian sports. Whilst retaining the spirit and courage of its ancestor, the Thoroughbred far exceeds it in size, speed, agility and stamina and it is thought that it can run as fast as is physically possible for any animal whilst carrying a man on its back.

Before the creation of the Thoroughbred, Europe's most famous breed was the Andalusian, a result of Oriental stock, brought over by the Moors in the eighth century, being crossed with Spanish ponies. These horses can be trained to an exceptionally high standard and they were in great demand on European battlefields during the Middle Ages. Other famous breeds have been established from it, most notably the Lippizaner. Lippizaner stallions are considered the best trained horses in the world and their exciting displays still contain many of the mediaeval cavalry exercises.

All the heavy draught breeds that are known as 'working horses', including the Great Horse of Europe, are descended from a sub-species of wild horse called the Forest Tarpan which looked similar to the modern Norwegian Dun. There are numerous draught breeds; the French Percheron, Austrian Prizganer, the English Shire which is the world's largest horse, and they come in a variety of colours. Few of these horses weigh less than a ton and their heights range between sixteen to nineteen hands. A Shire can pull up to five tons and remarkably enough has an extremely docile nature.

There are numerous varieties of ponies, in cold and warm countries. Colour, shape and temperament vary (although all display more than a hint of stubbornness); the only criterion for calling a horse a pony is that, unless it is an Arabian, it should be less than 14.2 hands in height. Usually

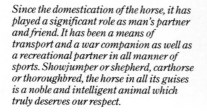

Since the domestication of the horse, it has played a significant role as man's partner and friend. It has been a means of transport and a war companion as well as a recreational partner in all manner of sports. Showjumper or shepherd, carthorse or thoroughbred, the horse in all its guises is a noble and intelligent animal which truly deserves our respect.

gentle, intelligent and very active, they have delightfully willing natures which make them excellent riding horses for children.

Equally good-natured but even more stubborn, the donkey also belongs to the horse family. The only major differences between the two are the half-haired tail, the upright mane and of course the larger, floppier ears, characteristics which it shares with certain other wild horses such as the zebra. Donkeys are small but sturdy and in many countries are still used to carry packs across country, especially in mountainous regions, where its sure-footedness makes stumbling a rare thing. In the paddock, if a new horse is brought in alone, the placid donkey can provide excellent companionship and a steadying influence if the horse is particularly nervous.

Horses, like most other animals, and humans, are inquisitive and they take an interest in whatever is going on around them. They are fond of company and much prefer to have other horses in the field with them.

Australia and the U.S.A.

Covering nearly three million square miles in total area, the wild and rugged plains of Australia combine to make up the largest island in the world. This is the land of bucking broncos, bareback riding and steer wrestling – the land where those ever popular television characters, the cowboys, really do exist, displaying a standard of riding that is of the very highest. Vast areas, sometimes larger

than countries, are uninhabited – the total population of Australia amounts to little over that of some of the world's capital cities – and herds of sheep and cattle roam freely within boundaries that are so wide that the grazing land available to them appears inexhaustible. The value of the horse in this massive, agricultural country is immeasurable. What better way to keep charge of an enormous herd of sheep than sitting astride the versatile, strong, reliable horse? The men responsible for looking after and rounding up the herds are called 'ringers' and live in the saddle for days on end. For the sake of comfort they adopt a riding posture very different from those who ride for pleasure and who therefore spend less time actually on the horse. They sit well back in the specially designed high pommeled saddles and so ride with their legs considerably straighter.

Named after its home state of New South Wales, the Waler is the national horse of Australia. Lack of interest in the past has rendered the horse virtually extinct twice in its history, but its future now looks more certain as its qualities are once again being taken into account. Many of the English heavy working breeds such as the Shire and Clydesdale have been imported into the country and, with equestrian sports obviously finding a popular niche in Australian society, Arabs and English Thorougbreds have been brought in as well.

The relationship between the people of Australia and their 'four legged friends' to whom they owe much of their livelihood, is a very special one. Despite the fact that many of the men spend much of their working lives in the saddle, immense pleasure is gained from being with horses in leisure time as well, not only from organised sporting activities but also impromptu races and shows. The competitors have fun and the horses benefit from an exciting, active life and owners who appreciate their value and treat them with respect and understanding.

Peace or pageantry–a horse seems at home in either circumstance. Cowboys and bucking broncoes, bareback riders and steer-wrestling horses, especially in America and Australia, can be seen as part of many colourful and exciting displays.

Horses are not native to America. The early Spanish settlers in the 16th century brought with them the noble Andalusian horses from their own country and with the help of their horses explored new territory. At first the horses were regarded with awe and suspicion by the local Indian tribes, but as the amount brought into the country increased they became accustomed to the animals and quickly learned their potential. Many were stolen and the notorious mounted Indian tribes that terrorised the Western settlers enjoyed a short, but memorable heyday.

Gradually the horses broke away from the captive environment, adapting successfully to feral life because of the vast areas of rich pastureland that covered most of the country. Eventually the Andalusian degenerated into groups of wild horses now called Mesteno or Mustangs.

In America, as in Australia, the inhabitants are indebted to the horse and it has become a major feature of their folklore. Without it, early pioneers would never have settled successfully and the 'Wild West' would have remained unexplored.

If ever you stop at a field of horses you will find that they usually come over to take a closer look. Horses sleep little, but spend a lot of time dozing—standing or lying half asleep with their eyes almost closed and their ears back. Foals need play as much as they need food and sleep as it is vital to their growing muscles and sense of coordination. Horses have a keen sense of sight and can see colours as we do! They are very perceptive to movement—an adaptation developed as a form of protection and dating back to wild ancestors.

In the Wild

Very few truly wild horses still exist. A small group of Przewalski's horses, named after the Russian explorer Colonel Przewalski who discovered them, roam the land bordering China and remote parts of Mongolia and Russia. All other horses that are called wild are actually feral; descended from domesticated breeds.

Watching any animal in its natural environment is undoubtedly the best way of understanding its basic social habits. It also proves an invaluable way of learning how to treat it if it is taken away from its natural environment and expected to live happily in an alien world such as a stable. The most basic instinct of the horse is that of the herd. A group of horses offer mutual protection, they accept leadership and are sociable animals that thrive best in the company of others. Young born into a herd quickly learn the skills necessary for survival and they also benefit from a secure environment in which they can enjoy the company of other foals. A unique social system which gives each member of the herd an order of precedence ensures that harmony is maintained and whilst an experienced mare takes charge of the overall running of the herd, the stallion keeps order and is the main protector from routine dangers.

Routine is an essential part of every horse's existence but ferals adapt their grazing and resting patterns according to the amount of food available. During the summer months grass is plentiful and the herd will graze in the morning and evening, the cooler parts of the day, choosing to rest in the afternoon when the sun is at its hottest and trouble from flies is at its worst. In winter however, grass is scarce, and any that is available contains little or no nourishment, so grazing is from the first signs of daylight through to the very last. Even then, by the time the succulent spring grass appears some of the horses may have died of starvation and the general health of the whole herd will be poor.

Foals are born in the spring when the mares have plenty of nourishing grass to provide healthy food for their infants. Up to the age of four, male foals are called colts and females fillies. Fillies are fortunate in that they

All domesticated horses belong to the same species and are descended from the Eurasian wild horse. There were however three subspecies of wild horse and in prehistoric times, man killed them for food. Few wild horses survive today. The

Mongolian or Przewalski's horse can be found on the borders of the great Gobi desert. It is a sturdy pony, dun-coloured to bay, with an erect mane and mealy muzzle. To save it from extinction breeding herds have been established in wildlife parks.

can remain with the herd they are born into for the rest of their lives, but this is not the case with the colts. There is room for only one stallion in a herd and as the colts mature they are chased away by the stallion leader to fend for themselves. Often they will form bachelor gangs with other young stallions and it is not until they are older and considerably wiser that they will challenge another for the leadership of a herd, because only stallions of equal rank will fight.

Domestic Horses

Man is one of the few animals who can adapt quickly to his environment – an environment which more often than not he changes himself. Other animals are not quite so readily adaptable and the horse is no exception.

Today, many people derive pleasure from owning their own horse, riding it and schooling it for fun, and entering gymkhanas and other shows. A stabled horse is far removed from its natural way of life and even those that have never lived in the wild will retain the same instincts of the herd existence. To own a horse it is therefore of utmost importance to understand its own particular nature and learn to treat it correctly. No horse or pony can remain in good condition and give of its best unless it is properly fed, groomed and exercised. These are the fundamental aspects of horse ownership and if carried out wrongly or not at all, the horse will deteriorate rapidly in health and personality.

Although the horse's association with man dates back some 5,000 years, few will instantly trust a human being. All horses have naturally nervous dispositions and are easily frightened by things they do not understand, are not clearly visible or make loud noises. In the wild these would be considered a threat to their personal safety and so in the stable they have to learn to be confident in their strange surroundings. A great deal of time must therefore be spent gaining your

Safety should always be a prime consideration when riding. Particularly important are the right footwear and a protective hat – neither of which restrict the exhilarating sense of freedom which comes from a gallop through the countryside or along the seashore.

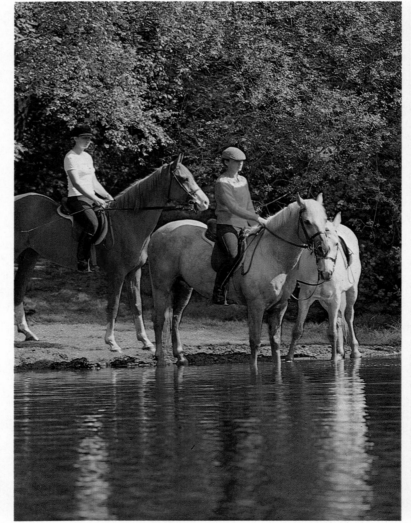

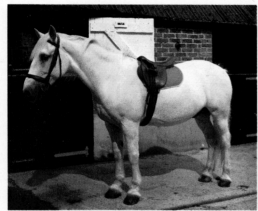

particular horse's trust, especially if it is a foal. It will not like being alone, nor will it feel safe with the various objects that surround it until it is gently introduced to them all. Kindly persuasion is the only treatment that will work with a horse. It will be instinctively terrified of dogs, noisy vehicles and anything else which is unfamiliar but if it learns to trust you, not only as a regular provider of food but also as a companion, half the battle will be won.

Many of a horse's natural attributes are to man's advantage in the early years of horse ownership. Its remarkable memory, readiness to obey and strong tendency to play 'follow my leader' make training that much easier. Once a horse has been taught a certain rule, it will remember it. It is important that its day to day life follows a regular pattern. It will look forward to seeing its owner at particular times of the day and will quickly distrust the person if these times are constantly altered. After schooling has started however, occasional breaks in training need not be a bad thing. A horse can get easily bored, which could lead to it developing a bad temper and selfish nature. More normally, any horse will have a very amenable personality and bad behaviour on its part is often a result of incompetent handling or rough treatment. As it is very sensitive to touch, punishment should be dealt out sparingly, but many horses do have a tendency to be greedy, for both food and attention. If a horse with this trait is constantly allowed to get its own way without any form of discipline it could become difficult to handle and unsafe to ride.

Understand your horse and communicate with it on the right level and it will give you its best, which is fun and exciting. If you are taking a horse into the home it really does involve a great deal of thought. There should not be odd mornings when you are late for work and are

Donkeys are also members of the horse family and have the same number of teeth as horses. Their appearance differs in the size and shape of the ears, the upright mane and the half-haired tail. Their placid nature makes them ideal companions for highly strung horses as they seem to have a steadying influence. These gentle creatures are very popular with children and will patiently plod up and down carrying small, and delighted, riders on their broad backs.

not able to attend to it, unless there is somebody else who the horse trusts and can do the job equally as well. A horse is a dependent animal from birth, and this dependence does not lessen as it grows older. A well looked-after horse will be happy and responsive and this should be the objective of every owner.

Creature Comforts

When grass first appeared on the plains, millions of years ago, the horse developed suitable teeth and a specialised digestive system to take full advantage of it. It is its natural food and a wild horse can live quite happily on grass alone. However, the nourishment gained from grass is only really sufficient for a horse to carry out its natural relatively lazy existence – keeping fit enough to flee from danger and to conduct other essential functions. But to do a good day's work it would not provide enough nourishment. Grass also has a high moisture content which blows out the stomach in such a way that strenuous exercise could cause problems with breathing. If a stabled horse is not a worker, four feeds a day mainly on hay should suffice. Good hay is as nourishing as spring grass and the lack of moisture in it is preferable. A horse's stomach is small, which accounts for the frequency of feeds and hay should be left in a rack in the stable at night to enable the horse to continue replenishing its stomach. The working horse needs a daily ration of grain, usually of crushed oats mixed with bran or chaff to make it more digestible, and salt, which is a vital part of its diet, should be provided in a holder. If a horse is living solely on dry food it would be a nice treat to bring some clover in for it, which grows during the summer months, and it would also enjoy a pound or two of apples or carrots (cut lengthwise for safety's sake) to vary what could become an extremely monotonous, although highly nutritious, diet.

Water is also an essential part of any animal's diet – and horses love it. It seems, when out riding, that whenever a horse comes across a pond or stream it will want to stop and drink, and many a mischievous school pony will stop and bend its

The natural time of year for both wild and domesticated horses to produce their foals is early summer when the new grass is especially lush and nutritious, providing maximum nourishment for the nursing mare. Between five and ten days from its birth, the suckling foal will also tentatively nibble at the grass, and anything else it can pick up in its mouth! Its natural inquisitiveness will lead to a thorough investigation of its surroundings.

head to take long, thirst quenching sucks of water for an interminable length of time, stubbornly resisting any attempts to get it moving again. A popular myth which surrounds horses and their drinking habits is that they should never be allowed to drink except before a feed. But this idea does date back to the days when horses were only taken out for a drink once or twice a day and so drank heavily all in one go. Certainly if a horse is allowed to drink a large amount after a feed it may get indigestion and it could be quite serious if the feed contained grain which swells in the stomach. It is also true that a wild horse will sometimes only drink once a day, but this is due to the high moisture content of the grass which is released slowly inside the body. It is perhaps not commonly realised just how much a working horse, if left to its own devices, will actually drink in one day. The amount does vary according to the climate but it will seldom be less than five gallons a day and some will drink as much as fifteen gallons. Fresh water (a horse will instinctively know if it is tainted and will avoid it however thirsty it may be) must therefore be offered in a bucket frequently, especially before each feed.

SHELTER is a comfort that is close to every horse's heart. An intense dislike of cold winds and heavy rain will send a horse off quickly in search of a protected area and in the summer constant irritation from flies may restrict it to shaded areas to escape the insects. A wild horse is fairly adept at protecting itself from the elements. Forests, gullies, even a single tree all provide some sort of shelter and in a herd horses will co-operate with one another in fending off flies by standing nose-to-tail side by side. Perhaps though, this is one area where man does have a lot to offer the horse. A warm, dry stable or even a shed in the paddock will not be refused, and carefully applied ointment to help keep the flies away will certainly be greatly appreciated.

SLEEP – Although it seems an impossibility to us, a horse really does sleep standing up. Its head will often nod contentedly as it rests and it will wake up and continue grazing a short

while later, apparently refreshed. Unlike other grazing animals a horse appears to need quite a lot of sleep, sometimes as much as seven hours in a full day. If it feels relatively safe from danger and the weather is warm it will often stretch out fully and have a slightly longer, deeper sleep, but it is always on the alert and will wake up at the slightest noise ready to flee immediately if necessary. Sleep is vital to a foal. It is the time, as with any infant, when most development takes place and it will stretch out full length on the ground falling into a deep sleep while its mother stands close by to protect it.

Horses At Play

All animals play. But it is not always easy to discriminate between 'play' and keeping fit, especially with adults. We may go swimming or play tennis in our leisure time but would not class these activities as play, even though they are enjoyable pastimes. A horse may canter round a field or kick the stable door for exactly the same reasons but we would almost certainly construe it as 'play' because it is not directly related with feeding, sleeping or grooming. Youngsters undeniably play, but even this is a vital way of learning skills that are required in adulthood as well as a means of establishing friendships, which are an important feature in the

A golden horse with a silver tail—it could only be a Palamino. Palamino is a colour rather than a breed and consequently the horse can be of any size. Arabians themselves are often Palaminos, as are several types of pony.

1

2

3

4

5

6

horse world. Many of the antics that foals indulge in enable them to find out the limitations and capabilities of their own bodies. An insatiable curiosity, which is shared by most youngsters, means that they will constantly be investigating their surroundings and, not content with just sniffing and circling small objects in an effort to identify them, will often try to pick them up and chew them, inevitably spitting them out again.

A foal on its own in a stable is not usually a happy sight. It will get easily bored and lonely without other foals or at least its mother to play with and will often amuse itself for hours by trying to stamp on its own tail or kick at the stable door just for the satisfaction of hearing the noise it makes.

Communication

It is only recently that we have realised just how important the powers of body language are. The remarkable way in which all animals, none of which possess such extensive means of vocal communication as we do, convey a variety of signals and emotions to one another that we cannot hear and often cannot even see, is all body language – a combination of postures and automatically produced chemicals that are instantly picked up by the one, or however many animals they are directed at. Horses use a great variety of facial expressions and physical gestures to make themselves understood. Nibbling the skin of another horse is a display of affection whereas baring the teeth and flattening the ears, a gesture most often seen between two stallions, is a sign of aggression.

The secretion of certain chemicals, most of which we cannot smell, plays a large part in mating and accounts for the fact that in the majority of mammals other than man, there appears to be very little of what we would actually call 'courtship'. The process of mating seems to be a very casual one with any preliminaries

A bright orange-brown horse with a mane and tail of roughly the same colour is known as a chestnut (7). Chestnut horses very often have patches of white on them, particularly on the face or legs. A small patch between the eyes is called a star and a streak from forelock to nose, a blaze.

virtually non-existent. This can be attributed to the means of communication by pheromones. Pheromones are naturally produced chemicals which greatly affect the behaviour of the animal and elicit certain responses from other members of the same species. By their production a stallion knows, therefore, when a mare is in season.

Mares And Foals

A foal endears itself to everyone. Only hours after birth, awkward legs struggle feebly to support the small fluffy frame and the foal will totter after the mother wherever she goes. With its soft-rounded muzzle and inquisitive nature – its face keenly observing every new event that occurs – few people can resist trying to stroke and feed one of these little creatures.

A mare carries her foal for about eleven months so it is born at a very advanced stage, able to walk soon after birth. In the wild this is of vital importance as the herd are constantly moving from one grazing area to another and if a foal was born totally helpless then its chances of survival in that particular environment would be slim. The following instinct, which appears to be innate in horses, is also vital just after the birth of a foal in helping to establish the parent-child bond which is of such importance in the early months. Mother and baby will learn to recognise the shape and smell of one another and eventually a mare will respond only to the cries of her own baby and similarly a foal will learn to react only when it is called by its own mother.

Naturally, horses are perfectly capable of foaling successfully in the wild with no human help whatsoever. This has been done for millions of years. But more often than not feral herds are kept a check on and the mares are taken from the herd when they are ready to foal and given the safety of a stable. A field shelter will suffice but if the birth is impeded a mare will quickly need expert attention. A foal is usually born after

The monarch among horses is generally considered to be the Arab. It is renowned for its elegance and beauty, and spirited yet gentle nature. It is the oldest and purest breed in existence today. In its native land, the Arabian peninsula, it has been pure-bred for over a thousand years!

a few hours labour and, if it is to survive, the birth must be quick. It will normally be released from the membranes and licked dry by the mare so that it is standing up and suckling within half an hour. Sometimes the afterbirth will not come away or the mare will be too weak to attend to the new-born so professional help, preferably the vet, must be sought.

For the first day or two, depending on the weather, a mare and her foal should be kept indoors and the mare should have access to plenty of rich, nourishing food. The foal will learn many basic skills by copying its mother and will be grazing with her only a few weeks after birth. Weaning takes place after about six months, although if the mare is allowed to remain with her foal she may continue to suckle it through the first winter until the appearance of the succulent green grass the following spring. Even if the foal is of a hardy breed it is advisable to keep it in a stable for that first winter if possible. Food is scarce and it is difficult for a horse to remain in good condition without travelling far and wide to find sufficient food.

In its natural environment a male foal, or colt, will remain with the rest of the herd until it is about four years old. It will then be chased away by the herd stallion until it is mature enough to look after a herd of its own. Females, or fillies, can stay with the herd for the rest of their lives.

A foal brought into the home should not be less than six months old unless it is still with its mother. If it has come from a free-living herd it will not only be lonely but frightened and unhappy in the sudden change of surroundings. If there are no other horses, or even a donkey or goat to keep it company for the early years of its life, a great deal of time should be devoted to it, earning its trust and providing very necessary friendship. Normally, an intensely curious nature and enjoyment of human attention

All modern light breeds of horses are related to the Arab, whose most distinctive feature must surely be its proud and graceful manner. The head is small and carried high and tapers from a broad, intelligent forehead to a small, delicate muzzle. The prominent eyes are large and expressive, the limbs are fine with a clean line, the coat is silky and the tail set high. The animal moves with a grace no other horse can match, but it also has tremendous speed and endurance over long distances.

will help it to adapt to its new environment. It derives great pleasure out of life and the more it is handled correctly, the more it will reward you with its trust and share with you its fun-loving nature.

Sporting Horses

Man and beast share many basic instincts, not least of which is a competitive nature. Both like to prove strength, courage and endurance over others and this is the desire which has led to sport being one of man's major leisure pursuits – and the involvement of animals, particularly horses, in it.

From the moment man first rode the horse, a race must have taken place. In Europe history dates the first equestrian sports to the times of the Roman Empire. The Romans loved sport although theirs was considerably more cruel than the

sport of today. As they spread through Europe establishing leadership in various countries they built hippodromes in which horsedrawn chariots raced speedily around. But the breed of horse used at that time was not specifically designed for fast running and it was not until the Arabians brought their own hot-blooded stoock into Europe, and they combined with the local breeds, that the standard of racing was raised. It was the cross-breeding

Horse racing is big business all over the world. Large prizes are offered, competition becomes fiercer all the time and, somehow, the horse gets faster and faster! Horse racing is a thrilling spectacle, wherever it takes place.

1

2

3

6

4

5

7

8

9

A horse with a more or less white coat is not called a white but a grey (6) and (8). Greys occur in many breeds from Arabs and Thoroughbreds to mountain breeds and Shetland ponies. Some greys appear nearly white, some attractively dappled, and some so dark that they are known as blue roan. Not all greys are born that colour–some are born almost black but are almost white when grown, such as the wild Carmargue horses in eastern France.

of the Arabian and the English breed that produced the most famous of all racing horses–the Thoroughbred.

Today flat racing and steeplechasing have a large public following. The first flat race in England was said to have been in 1174 during the reign of Henry II and it was probably run in heats over a distance of four miles, as were the majority of early races. But this length of run quickly exhausted horses and rarely gave the public the excitement of a fast finish. Gradually the distance was reduced and in modern races many of the Classics are run over a mile and a half or two miles. In Britain several classic races are run each year, including the English Derby, regarded as the greatest test for a three-year-old over one and a half miles, the Oaks and the St Leger. All three were first run in the latter part of the 18th century. Racing is also a popular sport elsewhere in the world. Australia and New Zealand have particularly good reputations and breed excellent horses. France now holds an eminent position in the racing world and the Poules d'Essai and Prix Royal are just two of the races in which top class riders compete.

The origins of the steeplechase, of which one of the most famous is the Grand National, date back to the days when the English countryside was considerably more rugged than it is today and casual races were organised between private individuals, often to settle a dispute over property or finance. The race ran between one village and the next, probably starting from one church steeple with the finishing point at the church steeple of the neighbouring village. These rides were across open country and involved jumping hedges, streams and gates to reach the finishing point by the quickest route. Later on, the races were arranged on a circular route so that the starting and finishing points were the same or nearby. Today, although point-to-point races are still held in country areas, steeplechasing itself is a highly organised activity held on an enclosed track and supervised by the National Hunt Committee. Artificial jumps which, excepting water jumps, must be at least 4ft 6ins high, test the horse's ability and endurance and the minimum length of a race is two miles, with twelve obstacles or more strategically placed at various distances along the course.

In both flat racing and steeple-chasing, the financial aspect is now enormous. Winners of the Classics stand to collect big prize money and the increasing demand for good quality horses has led to high prices being paid for potential winners. Combined with this is the undeniable entertainment value of these sports and the resulting growth of the betting industry which now has a multi-million pound turnover every year.

Another popular equestrian sport is Polo – one of the fastest team games in the world and probably the most masterful. The name Polo is derived from the Tibetan word 'pulu' meaning a ball, and it is most likely that the game itself originated in Persia and India many centuries ago, where it was played on any open patch of ground with rules varying from district to district. The British Regiment, stationed in India in the 19th century discovered that polo was not only an enjoyable game, but an excellent way of teaching young cavalry officers good horsemanship. In 1868 the first match in England was played on Hounslow Heath. The ponies used were small – about 12½ hands high, and the rules were sketchy. Today the game, as with all equestrian sports, is highly organised and exciting to watch. It involves two teams of four who must remain in the saddle whilst hitting a small ball with a mallet from a galloping pony with an opponent constantly attempting to thwart the procedure. Points are scored by hitting the ball between the correct goal posts set at either end of a grass pitch three hundred yards by two hundred yards in size. A good polo pony, now much larger than the originals used on Hounslow Heath, is difficult to train and therefore expensive to buy. It is not mature or strong enough to train until the age of five after which it takes a year to teach it the game and a further year of using it in minor matches before it is ready to compete in the more important games.

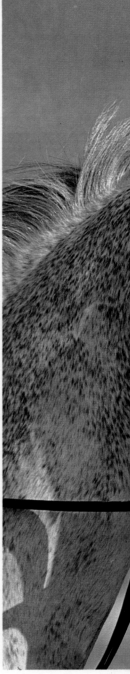

Trotting (2) is a form of light cart racing which is popular in America, Australia and Russia although it has never really caught on in Britain. It can be a very exciting spectacle and it requires great skill.

8

9

6

7

10

Show-jumping

Show-jumping is a relative newcomer to the equestrian sporting world. Towards the end of the 18th century it was referred to in a French cavalry manual but it was not until the 1860's that organised show-jumping events were held.

It is a popular sport, open to adults and children and fun to watch, especially at professional levels. Numerous gymkhanas are held every year in which jumpers of all standards can compete against others of similar achievement, whilst organised professional competitions are held for the experienced jumpers.

It is wrong to assume that horses naturally jump to the height required of them in the professional show ring. All animals enjoy jumping – and some can jump higher than others – but a real show-jumping horse must have the ability to consistently clear six foot fences and so is a highly specialised individual in the equine world. Temperament is also an important factor in whether a horse has the qualities of a champion, and a great deal of time and patience is needed in sorting out the potentials from the non-starters.

The popularity of the sport can be attributed to a number of things. If the fences are of a height that require horses to give of their best to jump them successfully, excitement can build up quickly. Clear rounds are possible but so are mistakes and the

Show jumping horses are very specialised individuals which must be capable of regularly clearing six-foot fences as well as having a steady temperament. Long hours of patient training, and expert riding, are essential if a horse is to reach its potential.

tension is high. It is also an easy competition for everybody to judge. Four faults for a fence down, three for the first refusal, six for the second and elimination for the third. In the event of several riders having achieved a clear round the overall winner may have to be decided by completing a further round 'against the clock'. There are basically four types of fence; the upright, the pyramid, the parallel and the staircase, and each should be designed to encourage a horse to jump to the best of its ability and not to trap it.

A three-day event, or Eventing, is closely connected with show-jumping, but many consider it to be a more thorough test of both horse and rider. The same mount is ridden throughout, and the three days consist of dressage on the first, cross-country, which is often the most rigorous section on the second, and show-jumping on the last day.

Haute Ecole could be considered the equestrian contribution to the art treasures of the world. A varied display of horses trained to an exceptionally high standard, it represents classical horsemanship at its most perfect and is pure delight to the eye.

In Italy, a little over four hundred years ago, Count Cesar Fiaschi established an advanced school of horsemanship with horses imported from Spain. Word of the school soon spread throughout the world and many famous monarchs, including Henry VIII were taught riding skills by Masters of the Horse from this school. By the time the Austrian Empire was at its highest a magnificent riding hall had been built in Vienna – the Spanish Riding School – to which riders from all over the world travelled to study methods of advanced training. Today it is still the most famous centre of Haute Ecole.

To a large extent the high standard of training achieved amongst the horses is due to their breed – Lippizaners, descended from the Andalusian horse and first bred for royal use. Only stallions are used in

Television coverage has done a considerable amount towards popularising the sport of show jumping. It is now watched by many people who have never ridden a horse and have no intention of doing so!

the Spanish Riding School and they
mature slowly, leading active lives for
many years. At the age of four,
training begins under the Riders of
the School and takes years to
complete. Each individual horse is
noted for its own particular talent for
various movements and will be
specially trained in these aspects for
display to the public. To the
accompaniment of music by Chopin,
Mozart and other composers,
spectacular demonstrations are
staged. Intricate patterns are woven
by groups of perfectly choreographed
horses under the glittering lights,
all performed with superb grace.

It may perhaps be thought that the
existence of the Spanish School is not
of particular relevance to ordinary
riders. But riding at any level is an art,
and all artists must have something to
aspire to – an ultimate goal which
represents perfection in that field.
The Spanish Riding School is that.

In all sporting events involving
horses it becomes apparent that a
high degree of training is required.
This training, far from deviating from
any natural abilities that horses
possess, nurtures them to produce
remarkable results. Driving is a sport
which is enjoying increasing
popularity and is somewhat set apart
from the others in that a well trained
carriage horse has to overcome a

*A riding horse that does not belong to any recognised
breed but somehow is of a definite type is known, in
Britain, as a hack. Colour is irrelevant but height and
temperament are of the utmost importance. High on the
list of attributes for a good riding horse are grace, intelligence
and willingness, and these can be detected at an early age.*

very basic instinct; its innate fear of being followed by something it cannot see, which in this case is the carriage, coach or gig that it is harnessed to. Harnessing several horses together for the purpose of pulling a vehicle happened early on in the domestication of horses, Greek and Roman charioteers probably being amongst the first to employ them this way. By the 18th century riding in a coach and four was a pleasurable and extremely fashionable mode of transport and today driving is popular all over the world not only as a sport but as a recreation. The horses, beautifully groomed and colourfully adorned, are trained to obey a variety of command signals and display great intelligence in allowing room for the carriage when turning through a gate. Competitions include riding rallies, scurry races and even a three-day event which is based on the pattern of the mounted one.

Hunting

The origins of hunting, the most controversial of all equestrian activities, lie in the green, pastoral American states of Virginia, Maryland and Pennsylvania, which were amongst the first to be colonised by the British. Public attitude towards the sport is almost invariably strong and can be split into two basic opinions: those who are pro the sport and those who are violently opposed, to the extent of engaging in bitter quarrels which often result in ambushing hunts. However, neither of these arguments concern the use of the horse in this activity, and there can be little doubt that a hunting party, with its magnificent horses, their riders clothed in scarlet, surrounded by a pack of excited baying hounds, is a colourful spectacle which recreates the atmosphere of a by-gone era.

In the breeding of horses specifically for hunting, Britain has not been as prolific as Europe, where there has been a greater degree of systematic selection of breeding stock. As a result the only real criterion that

Whether or not we consider hunting a desirable sport, there is little doubt that it makes a colourful and exciting spectacle. The full regalia of scarlet coat, polished boots and hunting horn echoes a strong tradition, as does the pomp and pageantry of Britain's mounted horseguards.

Man has a unique and very special relationship with the horse, a relationship which has grown steadily since the animal's domestication. It has held a special place in many of man's early cultures and also in the realm of art, where it has inspired artists and sculptors throughout the centuries, all over the world.

exists for a horse being classified as a hunter seems to be that it is actually used for hunting, regardless of its shape, size and colour. Ideally a hunter should be of a reasonable height and should be partially Thoroughbred – not only to give it agility and intelligence but, perhaps most importantly of all, tremendous stamina.

Police Horses

Many of the duties that were carried out by the first mounted police in 1763 are now undertaken by motorised vehicles such as cars, helicopters and motor cycles, but there are still many aspects of police work for which the horse is invaluable. For controlling large crowds and leading processions no vehicle can provide such gentle yet imposing force and perhaps just the sight of a policeman astride so great an animal in itself acts as a deterrent. One obvious feature which qualifies a horse for police work is its size – few small ponies could have such impact on a large crowd. But size alone is not enough. These horses must have the intelligence to be trained to a very high standard. They must learn to overcome many basic fears and not flee from loud noises, confused crowds and hazards such as smoke and fire. At training school they are introduced to these various things and patiently taught to walk quietly and maintain a controlled calm in any situation. Above all they must not panic. The mount, when dealing with such specialised horses, must be highly trained in how to handle them, so that a special relationship of mutual trust exists between horse and rider.

The Farrier

All horses, in whatever walk of life, from the riding pony to a top class show-jumper, need constant care and attention. For medical matters the most qualified person to consult is the vet, but practically anything else concerning the equipment of the horse can be handled by a farrier. Until recently few towns and villages were without their local 'smithy' but the outbreak of the Second World War brought about increased mechanisation in order to meet the demand for home-grown produce. Farriers found that their particular skills were required less and less and were eventually forced to find work elsewhere. As a result the craft became in grave danger of dying out. Today, with the pleasures of riding rediscovered and an increase in the amount of horses being bred, the farrier is once again in great demand. Unfortunately few are to be found as it takes years to learn the trade to a high standard, and those who are working are usually too busy to take on an apprentice and devote the time necessary for training. But however far must be travelled to find a blacksmith, it is essential that a horse is attended by one several times a year, preferably once a month. A horse's feet are of the utmost importance and loose shoes, cracked hooves and splinters can cause untold damage, possibly leading to permanent lameness. Regular inspections of the feet, trimming and shaping of the hooves and re-shoeing are therefore essential from time to time. Shoeing a horse is not as painful as it may appear to the observer. The hooves are cleaned with knives and filed down before a shoe is heated until red-hot and held against the hoof so that any irregularites which remain are shown up by charring. The shoe is then shaped to fit and attached with nails to the hoof.

These days, a good farrier is not very easy to come by, but he is essential to the wellbeing of a horse (2). A horse should really be attended to once a month as its feet are of paramount importance. It is not simply a question of replacing an old, worn shoe, but of trimming and shaping the hoof and inspecting it for any problems. Nowadays, several farriers operate a travelling service.

4

5

6

First English edition published in 1981 by Colour Library International Ltd.
This edition is published by Crescent Books, Distributed by Crown Publishers Inc.
Illustrations and text © : Colour Library International Ltd. 163 East 64th Street, New York 10021.
Colour separations by FERCROM, Barcelona, Spain.
Display and text filmsetting by Focus Photoset, London, England.
Printed by Cayfosa and bound by Eurobinder - Barcelona (Spain)
All rights reserved.
Library of Congress Catalog Card Number: 81-67585
CRESCENT 1981

Dep. Leg. B. 3.125/82